9.

MODULAR SCIENCE
SE

G000140686

MODULE 2 *Pollution*

*Do you think there is a link between watching the TV and releasing poisonous gases into the air? Many aspects of everyday life can damage the environment – this type of damage is called **pollution**. This module looks at pollution and how to avoid it.*

Relevant National Curriculum Attainment Targets: 5, (2)

2.1 What is pollution?

Pollution

The environment in which you live contains many different organisms. One way or another, these organisms depend on each other and the world around them in order to stay alive. All living organisms produce waste materials – often this waste is used by plants so they too can stay alive. Only a few waste materials can be used in this way. Most other forms of waste damage the environment – this is what is meant by **pollution**.

Most pollution is caused by humans, but there are a few other sources of pollution.

How can pollution be harmful?

If you throw away a chocolate wrapper, you may be harming the environment. In Great Britain, nearly 1 million tonnes of rubbish are produced each week. A lot of that rubbish does not end up in the dustbin. It is left lying around, polluting the environment.

Other types of pollution can be deadly. If waste from certain factories gets into the rivers, many animals will be poisoned. Poisonous gases from cars and chimnies can spread through the air and kill trees in forests thousands of miles away.

Even when only a few people drop litter, it soon builds up.

The brown spots were caused by the chemical pollution which killed these fish.

'Dead wood' – poisoned by long-range air pollution.

What a waste!

Power stations produce the electricity that we all like to use – but they also produce waste. Coal is burnt in power stations to make electricity. As it burns, the coal releases poisonous gases into the air. This waste can pollute the environment.

The process of making electricity involves heating large quantities of water. This hot water is often pumped into rivers while it is still warm. This waste heat then kills many organisms that live in the rivers. Some countries do not let this hot water go to waste. Can you think how the hot water could be used?

There are many other types of pollution which could be avoided if the waste was put to good use.

Pollution can be hard to detect – there's no smoke, but the river may still suffer.

It's the tall thin chimneys of power stations that pollute the air.

What needs to be done?

Be more aware of your environment – watch out for things that might pollute it. Remember that pollution is harmful to the many organisms living there – including you!

What things should you look out for? Thick dust and smoke are a sure sign of air pollution. Oily water or dead fish in a stream show water pollution. But only a few types of pollution are easy to see. Much dangerous waste goes unnoticed – until it is too late.

This module will help you to find out more about pollution – its causes, its effects and what to do to stop it.

If this field gets polluted, the poison can pass from the plants to the cows and to you!

2.2 Take care of the air

What is air pollution?

If smoke pollutes the air, it is easy to see. This is because it contains black particles of carbon which are known as soot. Other pollutants are invisible gases like sulphur dioxide and carbon monoxide. You can't see them, so the air might look clean, but they can poison you.

Not all invisible gases are poisonous, but they can still be pollutants – carbon dioxide is one example. Air pollution can be due to many different pollutants. In each case it means that the air contains some chemical which is not normally found there.

Air pollution – making a mess of the air you breathe.

Where does it come from?

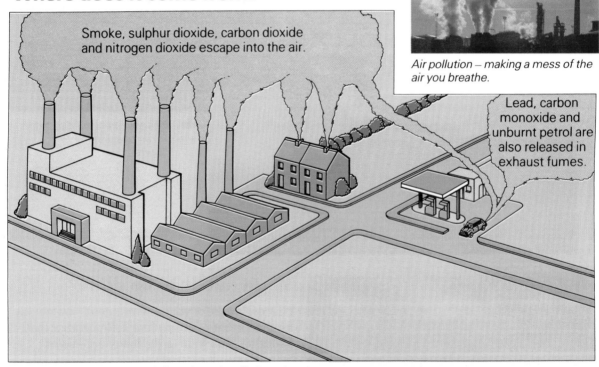

Smoke, sulphur dioxide, carbon dioxide and nitrogen dioxide escape into the air.

Lead, carbon monoxide and unburnt petrol are also released in exhaust fumes.

Fuels like coal, oil and petrol all produce air pollution when burnt.

How much pollution is there?

Often there only needs to be a tiny amount of a pollutant to make the air polluted. The level of pollution is found by measuring the mass of pollutant present in a standard volume of air. The mass of the pollutant is measured in **microgrammes** (μg) – one millionth of a gramme. The standard volume of air is **one cubic metre.**

These measurements can be used to compare one area with another. The amount of air pollution can vary quite a lot from area to area.

Air Pollutant	Amount of air pollutant in microgrammes per cubic metre of air	
	Area A	Area B
sulphur dioxide	80	25
lead	1300	50
smoke	110	25
nitrogen dioxide	321	119
carbon monoxide	106	33

Which area would you prefer to live in?

Air pollution and health

You are continually breathing air into your lungs. This means your lungs are the most likely part of your body to suffer from the effects of air pollution. Bronchitis is a type of lung disease – the numbers of deaths it causes are shown in the top graph.

Can you see a connection between the deaths from bronchitis and the distance from a city centre?

The bottom graph shows that the closer you get to the city, the greater the amount of sulphur dioxide pollution in the air. Some people have suggested that there is a connection between the deaths caused by bronchitis and the level of sulphur dioxide pollution. Do you agree with this idea?

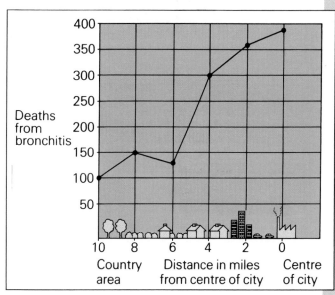

Where is the greatest risk of suffering bronchitis?

Other pollutants

There are many poisonous pollutants in the air – such as mercury and cadmium from industrial sources, lead from car fumes. These can get from your lungs into your blood. These pollutants build up slowly until they reach poisonous levels. They are called **cumulative poisons.**

Prevention is the only cure!

Nowadays, the amount of smoke produced when burning fuels has been greatly reduced. For example, natural gas is a smokeless fuel used in many homes and factories. Solid fuels are also available which produce very little smoke. But they are more expensive than coal which produces sooty smoke. This is because they have to be treated in a special way. There is also lead-free petrol on sale. Although it is cheap to produce, it cannot be used in all types of cars.

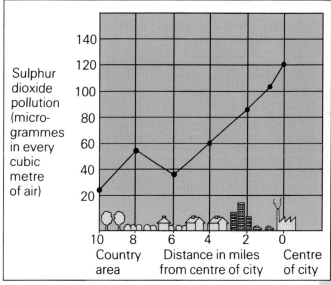

Hot waste gases from tall chimneys often cool and fall in quite short distances.

1 Why can't you always see air pollution? What kinds of air pollution can be seen?

2 Name two poisonous gases that are air pollutants.

3 Look at the table opposite:
   a What units are used to measure air pollution?
   b Which pollutant is found in the largest amounts? What causes it?
   c Which area (A or B) is nearer to a city? Give a reason for your answer.

4 a Name two fuels which cause sulphur dioxide pollution.
   b Give two examples of cumulative poisons that are air pollutants.
   c How do these poisons get into your body?

5 a What is unusual about the number of bronchitis deaths 8 miles from the centre of the city?
   b Can you suggest a reason for this? (*Hint:* what goes up, must come down!)

2.3 *Acid rain, a deadly downpour*

'Vinegar rain'

The vinegar you put on your fish and chips tastes bitter. It is a **weak acid** – a chemical which turns indicator paper red. But you don't just find weak acids in vinegar bottles – you can find them in the air too!

Once there was a rainstorm in the USA with rain that was 1000 times more acidic than vinegar. This type of rain is known as **acid rain**.

What goes up, must come down

Every time you switch on the TV, you are helping to produce acid rain. The electricity you use is produced in power stations by burning fuels such as coal and oil. Travelling in cars or buses causes acid rain too. This is because of the fuel burnt in the engine.

When these fuels are burnt, gases such as sulphur dioxide, nitrogen dioxide and carbon dioxide are produced. If these gases dissolve in rainwater in the air, acid rain is formed. The strengths of different acids can be compared using a special scale called the **pH scale**. Vinegar has pH number of about 5. Distilled water is not at all acidic – it is *neutral*, with a pH of 7.

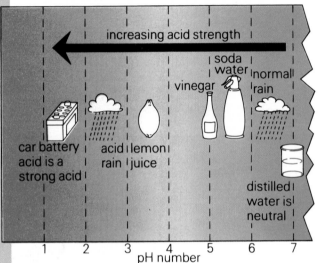

The lower the pH value, the stronger the acid.

Eating away

What do the pictures below tell you about the effect acid rain has on stone? Some metals such as iron and zinc are used on the outside of many buildings. These metals are also affected by acid rain – they lose their shine and become weak and brittle.

On the left is a stone figure on the wall of Lincoln Cathedral. On the right is the same figure 70 years later.

Innocent victims

If acid rain eats away at stone and rock, what must it be doing to living things? Large amounts of acid can kill. When acid rain falls, it collects in rivers and lakes, making the water acidic. All the living things in some lakes have been killed by acid rain. The small animals and plants in the water die first. Then the fish die too – and so do all the other animals, which feed on them!

Trees also suffer from the effects of acid rain. In Europe, large areas of forest are dead or dying as a result of acid rain.

Should power stations avoid burning fuels which produce acid rain?

Curing the problem

Efforts have already been made to make lakes less acidic. One way of doing this is to add lime to the lake water. Lime is an **alkali** – a chemical which reacts with acids and makes them weaker. When lime is added, the lake water becomes less acidic and its pH increases. If more acid rain falls into the lake, more lime must be added.

The best way to prevent acid rain is to stop the gases which cause it from escaping into the air. In power stations, this is now done by passing all the waste gases through an alkaline solution. This is called **scrubbing** and removes the gases which cause acid rain. Car exhausts can be fitted with **converters** which change nitrogen dioxide (one cause of acid rain) into harmless nitrogen.

This truck is spraying lime powder into a lake to reduce the acidity caused by acid rain.

These methods of limiting air pollution are quite effective, but may make electricity and cars more expensive. A choice may have to be made – either to save money or else to help to save the environment.

1 What is the pH number for lemon juice?

2 Which is the stronger acid – lemon juice or acid rain?

3 Otters feed mainly on fish. Why would otters be affected by acid rain?

4 If you want to stop acid rain, why is "scrubbing" gases from a power station better than adding lime to lake water?

5 How would animal life in a forest be affected by acid rain?

2.4 Nature's warning signs

Are you breathing clean air?

The air you are breathing may contain particles or gases that can damage your health. But how can you tell? In Tokyo, the pollution is so bad that there are large electronic scoreboards in public areas. These scoreboards show people the amount of pollution in the air they are breathing!

Watch out for pollution!

There are simpler, natural ways of detecting pollution. Plants called **lichens** can show how much pollution there is in the air.

Bushy lichens need really clean air. They are easily poisoned by just a small amount of sulphur dioxide. If you have this lichen growing near you the air will probably be very clean.

Leafy lichens can put up with a small amount of air pollution. If you can find this lichen growing on tree bark, the air is probably quite clean.

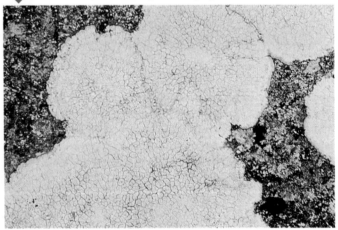

Crusty lichens are able to survive in air polluted with sulphur dioxide. They can be found growing on trees and walls in most town centres.

If there are *no lichens* around the air must be heavily polluted with sulphur dioxide.

A tough life

Lichens grow in very exposed places. Not many plants can grow on the dry surface of rocks or tree bark. To grow in such places, lichens need to be very good at **absorbing** water and nutrients. They get these by absorbing any rainwater which falls on them. Rainwater contains very small amount of nutrients which are just enough to keep the lichens alive.

Taking in poison

When the air is polluted, rainwater contains more than just small amounts of nutrients. It also contains poisonous pollutants, such as sulphur dioxide. For many lichens, absorbing polluted rainwater is the same as absorbing a poison.

Some lichens can stand quite a high level of sulphur dioxide, but others are poisoned when there is just a trace of the gas in the air. This means that the presence of lichens can provide you with a clue of how much pollution there is in the air – they are **pollution indicators**.

Studying pollution

This map shows the results of a study of lichens found in a particular area. Study the map carefully and then answer the questions below.

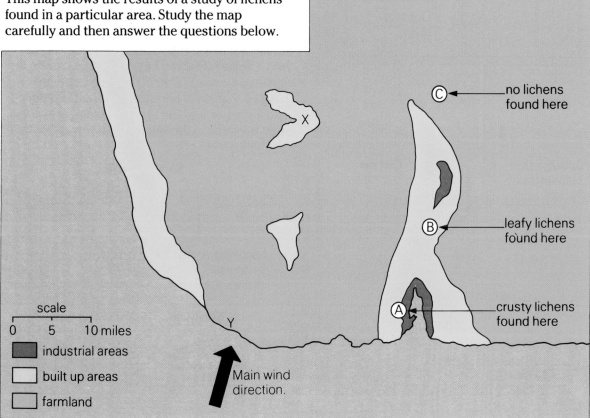

scale
0   5   10 miles

industrial areas

built up areas

farmland

C ← no lichens found here

B ← leafy lichens found here

A ← crusty lichens found here

Main wind direction.

1 What sort of lichen grows only in areas of almost no pollution?

2 How do lichens get enough water and nutrients to grow in very dry places?

3
a Which area on the map above (A, B or C) shows the highest level of air pollution? Give a reason for your answer.
b Even though the two industrial areas produce the same amount of pollution, the pollution in this area is higher than elsewhere. Why do you think this is so?

4 What lichens would you expect to find in
a region X
b region Y?
In each case explain your answer.

5 When the sulphur dioxide pollution in an area was reduced, it took years before the lichens growing in the area showed any change. What reasons could you suggest for this delay?

Pulling the plug out

What would your life be like if you had no water supply to your home? You would soon realise just how essential water is in your daily life. You use it for drinking and cooking. You wash yourself and your clothes in it and you use it to flush the loo. The water that has been used becomes smelly, filthy and full of harmful bacteria. When you pull the plug out or flush the loo, where does all this filthy waste go?

Fighting the filth

All the waste water is flushed from your home into a **sewer**. This is a large pipe that carries the waste to a sewage works. Here the waste is **treated** to make it harmless before it is pumped into a river or into the sea. This diagram shows what happens to the waste in the sewage works.

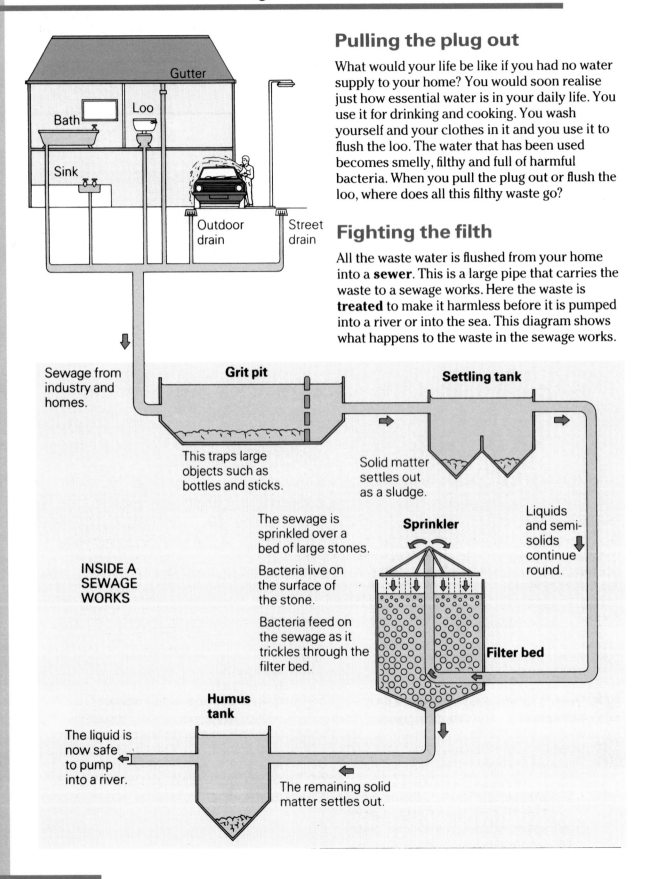

Gutter

Bath

Loo

Sink

Outdoor drain

Street drain

Sewage from industry and homes.

Grit pit

This traps large objects such as bottles and sticks.

Settling tank

Solid matter settles out as a sludge.

Liquids and semi-solids continue round.

The sewage is sprinkled over a bed of large stones.

Bacteria live on the surface of the stone.

Bacteria feed on the sewage as it trickles through the filter bed.

Sprinkler

INSIDE A SEWAGE WORKS

Filter bed

Humus tank

The liquid is now safe to pump into a river.

The remaining solid matter settles out.

Preventing disease

Untreated sewage may contain bacteria that can cause serious diseases such as cholera or typhoid. In this country, sewage is made harmless before it is poured into a river. The treatment of sewage prevents the spread of such diseases by killing the bacteria that cause the disease. In many countries, human waste (faeces and urine) is put straight into rivers. The same river may be used to provide drinking water for many people. When the waste of one person suffering from typhoid gets into river water, hundreds of other people can become infected.

Diseases can spread rapidly if drinking water is polluted with untreated sewage.

Food for bacteria – death to fish

As well as being a health hazard, untreated sewage can also damage the environment. When untreated sewage is put into a river, it becomes food for **decomposing bacteria**. These are bacteria that obtain their energy from dead or waste material. To release energy from sewage, the bacteria need oxygen. The effect this has on the river can be seen in this diagram. ▼

Clean water containing plenty of oxygen and a wide variety of animals.

Bacteria use up oxygen as they break down the sewage. Fish and many other animals die because of a shortage of oxygen.

Sewage continues to be broken down as the river carries it along. It may be carried a long way downstream before the river returns to normal.

1 Name four main stages in the treatment of sewage.

2 Name two diseases that can be spread by untreated sewage.

3 Sometimes sewage contains poisonous pollutant substances produced by industry. What effect could this have on the working of the filter bed?

4 In some sewage works, air is blown through the sewage after it has passed through the settling tanks. Why does this help to treat the sewage?

5 Why do fish die when untreated sewage is added to rivers?

This river is obviously polluted but it is not always so easy to tell.

Testing for pollution

How can you tell that the water in a river is polluted? The water may look clean but it could contain harmful substances that will kill all the life in the water. The most common substance that pollutes rivers is **sewage**.

Sewage can kill aquatic life by removing oxygen from the water (for more details, see pages 40 and 41). The oxygen is used up by bacteria which feed on the sewage. If a river contains only a small amount of oxygen, it is a sign that it may be polluted by sewage. The amount of oxygen can be measured using an oxygen meter.

Pollution clues

You can also use the presence of certain animals to tell you about the state of a river. When the amount of oxygen falls, some animals will swim away and others will even die. Only a few animals that can live in low levels of oxygen will stay. The animals that can be found indicate whether the river is clean or polluted. They are **indicator animals**.

A similar lack of oxygen is caused by the waste from paper factories and food factories. The bacteria can also feed on this waste and again cause the oxygen level to fall.

A selection of indicator animals.

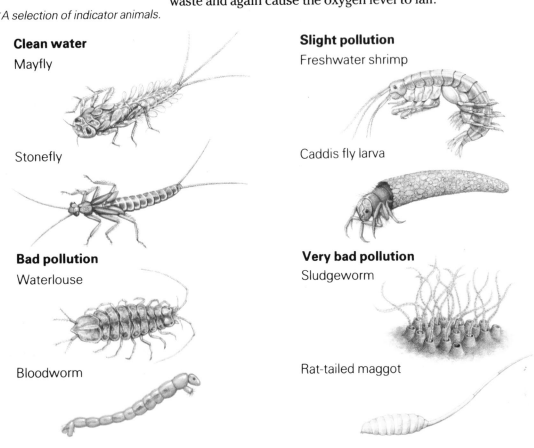

Clean water
Mayfly

Stonefly

Bad pollution
Waterlouse

Bloodworm

Slight pollution
Freshwater shrimp

Caddis fly larva

Very bad pollution
Sludgeworm

Rat-tailed maggot

What's more ...

There are many other pollutants which simply poison the water directly. Some of these come from modern farming methods. Others are due to waste from homes and factories.

Phosphates and nitrates are chemicals which are used as fertilisers to help crops grow. Before long, rainwater washes them into streams where they poison the animal and plant life. While solving one problem in farming, the fertilisers help to create a pollution problem!

Many soaps also contain types of phosphates. As well as 'bars' of soap, these phosphates are found in washing-up liquid, washing powder and shampoos. The sewage system is not always able to remove these soaps and they end up polluting the rivers and streams.

Engine oil, diesel and petrol are very damaging pollutants. These substances should *never* be poured down a drain. Even spilling them on the soil can cause problems to the water supply. Most councils have a special arrangement for people who want to get rid of old oil and fuel.

Keeping it all in check

There are strict controls which stop factories from polluting the sewage system. Scientists from Water Authorities have to keep a careful check on river pollution. There's a lot to watch out for! Poisonous metals such as arsenic and nickel; dust such as cement powder – in addition to all the sewage, oil, litter, nitrates and phosphates.

Anyone caught polluting the rivers or sewage system will have to pay a large fine. Over many years, the threat of being fined by the Water Authority has helped to stop people from polluting the water supply.

Fertilisers increase plant growth – and water pollution!

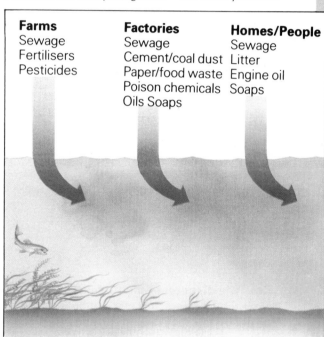

Farms	Factories	Homes/People
Sewage	Sewage	Sewage
Fertilisers	Cement/coal dust	Litter
Pesticides	Paper/food waste	Engine oil
	Poison chemicals	Soaps
	Oils Soaps	

Fighting water pollution involves controlling all these threats – and many more.

---

1 What two methods can be used to test for sewage pollution?

2 Name two animals that show that a river is very clean and two that show it is very polluted.

3
  a Give two possible causes of low oxygen levels in a river.
  b Explain how *one* of these actually reduces the oxygen level.

4 Describe two ways in which phosphates pollute rivers and streams.

5 Suppose a river contains a lot of mayflies and stoneflies at point A. Downstream at point B, there were only bloodworms and sludgeworms. What could have caused this difference? Explain your answer as fully as possible.

2.7 Protecting life in the sea

Oil means troubled waters

Oil is a major water pollutant. It is lighter than water and so floats on the surface. Oil pollution at sea is very harmful to sea-birds like the Guillemot in the photograph. When sea-birds dive into polluted sea-water to catch fish they become coated in a layer of oil. The oil clogs their feathers so that they cannot fly. The damaged feathers can no longer keep the birds warm and many die from the cold. Others are poisoned by the oil because they swallow it as they try to clean themselves.

Where does the oil come from?

Huge quantities of oil are transported all around the world in very large tankers. If one of these tankers has an accident, large slicks of oil soon spread across the surface of the sea. Oil slicks can have a very damaging effect on the sea and sea shore.

Four ways to clean up

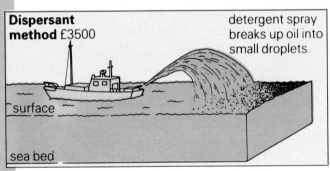

Dispersant method £3500
detergent spray breaks up oil into small droplets.
surface
sea bed

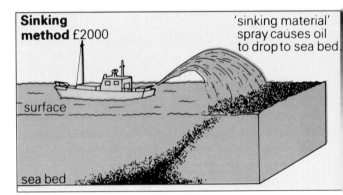

Sinking method £2000
'sinking material' spray causes oil to drop to sea bed.
surface
sea bed

▲ The **dispersant method** needs a few days before the oil clears. It is efficient but expensive. The detergents may poison fish and other animals and plants.

The **boom and skimmer method** gathers the oil up using a long barrier called a boom. A skimmer then scoops the oil off the surface into a suitable container. ▼

▲ The **sinking method** is quick and protects birds and beaches. However the oil pollutes the sea-bed and may even get washed ashore.

Shore cleaning is a last-stop measure. The sea has already been polluted and detergents and mechanical shovels are used to clean the beach.

Boom method £1000
boom positioned to scoop oil along surface.
surface
sea bed

Large scale pollution

An oil slick can be very difficult to control. It moves with the wind and the tides and can threaten a whole coastline.

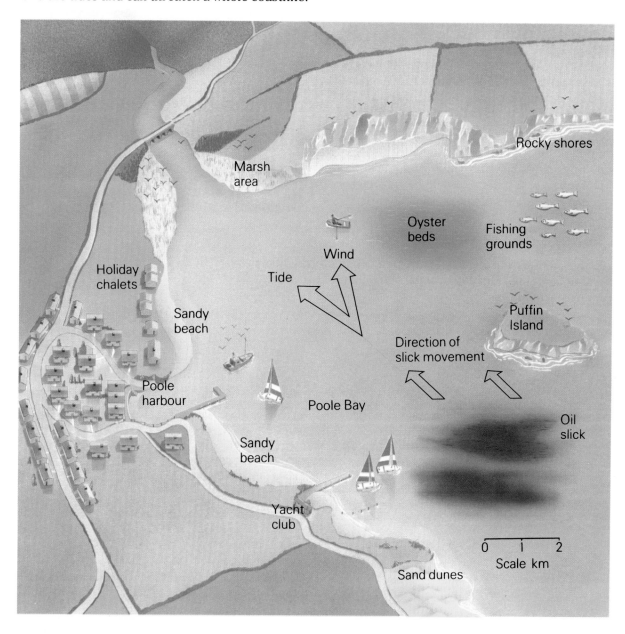

1 **a** Why is floating oil so dangerous to seabirds?
   b How does oil kill them?

2 Why does oil float on the surface of the water?

3 **a** Make a list of the areas around Poole Bay that will be affected by the oil slick.
   b Explain how oil will affect each area.

4 **a** Which method of control would you use to protect the birds nesting on Puffin Island?
   b What problems could this method of control have in other areas?

5 The pollution control officer has £4500 to spend to protect the whole of Poole Bay. Explain how you would spend this money to protect the Bay in the best way possible – don't ignore the disadvantages.

What are industrial pollutants?

Industry makes many of the things you need, but it also produces waste. Some factories release **waste particles** into the air as either dust particles or particles of heavy metals.

Other industries release **waste gases** such as sulphur dioxide into the air. Industry also pollutes rivers and tips with **liquid** and **solid wastes** such as detergents and heavy metals. These are all types of industrial pollutants.

Tall chimneys are used to release waste gases as far off the ground as possible.

Where do they come from?

Power stations, chemical industries, cement factories, quarries and the farming industry are some of the main sources of industrial pollution.

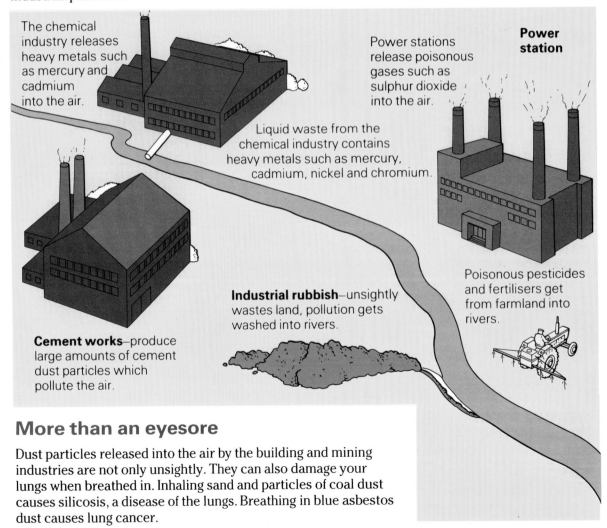

The chemical industry releases heavy metals such as mercury and cadmium into the air.

Power stations release poisonous gases such as sulphur dioxide into the air.

Power station

Liquid waste from the chemical industry contains heavy metals such as mercury, cadmium, nickel and chromium.

Industrial rubbish—unsightly wastes land, pollution gets washed into rivers.

Poisonous pesticides and fertilisers get from farmland into rivers.

Cement works—produce large amounts of cement dust particles which pollute the air.

More than an eyesore

Dust particles released into the air by the building and mining industries are not only unsightly. They can also damage your lungs when breathed in. Inhaling sand and particles of coal dust causes silicosis, a disease of the lungs. Breathing in blue asbestos dust causes lung cancer.

Useful but harmful

Heavy metals have many uses in industry. Nickel, chromium and cadmium are used to stop steel from rusting. The largest use of cadmium is in making long lasting nickel-cadmium batteries for the electronics industry.

These metals are **carcinogens** – this means they are chemicals which cause cancer. Mercury is another heavy metal and is used in many industrial processes. If it is breathed in, it builds up in the body and causes liver, kidney and brain damage.

A serious case of mercury poisoning occured in Japan about 20 years ago. Mercury pollution from a factory became concentrated in the flesh of fish in the area. Fish was the main food of the villagers living nearby. The more fish they ate, the more mercury the villagers took into their bodies.

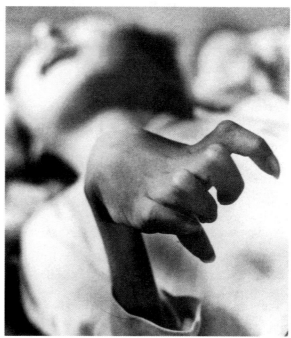

This Japanese child's hand shows a typical deformity caused by mercury poisoning.

Looking out for clean air

One method of monitoring dust pollution is to suck air through filter papers. The light reflected off the filter paper is then measured.

A filter paper with no dust on it reflects 100% of the light. The table shows the light reflected from samples of filter paper at different places.

Heavy metals are not so easy to detect. People working with heavy metals have to be especially careful. Their work area needs to be well ventilated if they are to remain healthy. Any waste gases need to be pumped away from the work place. They can then be treated before being released into the air.

Place	Filter paper	% light reflected from filter paper
(clean filter paper)	○	100
site A	○	96
site B	●	40
site C	◐	71
site D	◔	76

Measuring dust pollution.

1 Name two sources of industrial pollution.

2 Name two diseases caused by dust particles.

3 Why has cadmium become an increasingly important pollutant in recent years?

4 Give two ways in which mercury can get into the body.

5 **a** Put the results in the table in the form of a bar graph
b Which site is probably located near to a cement works? Give a reason for your answer.

6 Suggest *another* method by which you could measure the amount of dust on the filter paper.

7 What other precautions do you think workers in the heavy metal industry should take?

2.9 Radioactive waste

What is a radioactive substance?

All substances contain energy. A radioactive substance releases some of its energy as invisible **radiation**. This radiation can be made up of *either* fast moving tiny particles *or* rays similar to radio waves.

Is this radiation dangerous?

The energy from radiation can damage living cells. It can cause leukaemia (cancer of the blood) and many other cancers. It can also cause mutations in sex cells which will then lead to babies with deformities.

Your body is exposed to this kind of radiation every day but only to very small amounts. Wood, granite, air and soil all contain some naturally radioactive substances. Sunlight also includes some harmful radiation.

These sources contribute to a **natural background radiation**. The amount of energy from background radiation is very small and the chance of your body being damaged is low.

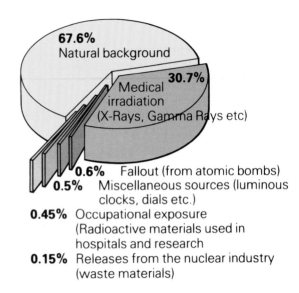

- **0.6%** Fallout (from atomic bombs)
- **0.5%** Miscellaneous sources (luminous clocks, dials etc.)
- **0.45%** Occupational exposure (Radioactive materials used in hospitals and research
- **0.15%** Releases from the nuclear industry (waste materials)

Which is the most common source of radiation you experience?

Wind blows dust to north and west

Radioactive dust gets into air

500 miles

Chernobyl
Nuclear power station catches fire

Not much radiation is needed to damage your health – so radioactive pollution from far away can still be a risk.

Increasing the risk

These days, some of the radiation that your body experiences is caused by our technology. Power stations and atomic bombs have produced radioactive waste materials. These have polluted our environment through leaks and fallout from explosions. In some places the level of background radiation may be no longer harmless.

The recent disaster at Chernobyl released massive amounts of radioactive waste into the air. Countries all over the world had to react very quickly to this pollution by checking drinking water and food for radioactive substances.

Even the radioactive sources used in hospitals, industry and research can be dangerous. In Brazil recently, an old hospital x-ray machine was damaged when left at a rubbish tip. Several people were taken seriously ill due to leaks from the machine's radioactive source.

There's always more...

Nuclear power stations continually produce radioactive waste. This has meant large amounts of nuclear waste have built up. These are increasing even faster now because more countries have started to use nuclear power to make the energy they need.

Low level waste include things such as clothing, containers and liquids. Some countries will not allow the large amounts of such low level waste to be dumped in their own country. This waste is often transported and dumped in other countries that do not have strict controls on pollution. Some of this waste is even dumped in the sea. But just getting rid of it does not mean it's safe!

Greenpeace supporters trying to prevent the dumping of nuclear waste at sea.

High energy waste

Some waste is very dangerous and will release large amounts of harmful radiation for thousands of years. This waste must be contained for a great length of time so that it cannot leak out into the environment. The nuclear industry spends vast amounts of money on the transport and storage of this waste in its attempts to prevent high energy waste pollution.

Guns have killed more people than have atomic bombs. Coal power stations continually produce waste gases that pollute the environment. But these facts do not mean that people and the environment are at less risk from nuclear weapons and nuclear power stations. Just because a risk is less common, it does not become less dangerous. Compare driving and flying – car accidents are much more common, but plane crashes are much more deadly.

Radioactive substance	How your body is affected
Strontium	Found in foods such as milk, cream and cheese. Absorbed into the production of bone cells. Linked with the disease leukaemia.
Caesium	Found in plants and animals (lamb, cows) that feed on plants. Linked with certain types of cancer.
Plutonium	An extremely poisonous substance. Tiny particles in the air settle in the lungs. Linked with lung cancer.

How radioactive waste can affect you.

1 You are exposed to radiation that comes from six main sources. What are they?

2 Draw a bar chart to show the amounts of radiation that come from the six main sources of radioactivity.

3 Name two radioactive substances and explain how they can affect your body.

4 The amount of radiation that your body receives each year is steadily increasing. Why do you think this is so?

5 What are the main problems with waste from nuclear power stations?

The case of the disappearing falcons

Peregrine falcons are magnificent birds of prey which feed on smaller birds, such as pigeons. These falcons attack their prey in a spectacular way, catching it in mid-flight. Peregrines have no natural enemies but their survival was once in doubt. How could this have been?

In the late 1950's, the number of peregrines suddenly decreased. If the number of these birds had kept decreasing, they would soon have disappeared completely. To prevent this from happening, it was necessary to find out why these birds were vanishing.

Peregrine falcons catch their prey in the air, but finish their meal on the ground.

Looking for clues

The scientists who noticed this decline had also made two other important observations. The first was that the number of peregrines had fallen more in some areas than others. In which areas had most of the peregrines died?

Their second observation was that dead pigeons were often found near fields which had been planted with wheat seed. In the 1950's farmers used to soak wheat seed in a chemical poison called **dieldrin**. This was done to prevent the seeds from being eaten by an insect called wheat bulb fly. Why do you think the pigeons were dying?

What effects could these deaths have on the peregrines living in the area? Do any of the scientists' observations support your ideas?

Death by poisoning

Only a little dieldrin was needed on each seed to kill the insect. The amount on one seed was not enough to kill a pigeon. But once a pigeon had eaten a lot of seeds, it would have eaten too much poison and would die. A peregrine suffered in a similar way when it ate poisoned pigeons.

The dieldrin poison even affected the birds long before they died. It made them lay eggs which would not hatch. The poison was killing both the adults and their off-spring at the same time.

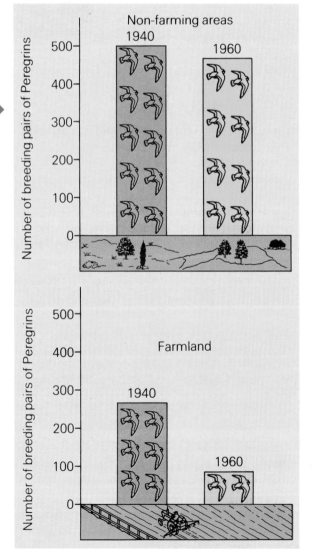

Why use chemical poisons?

Every year, large amounts of chemicals are sprayed on the soil or over crops by farmers all over the world. All together, the cost runs into millions of pounds. Many of the chemicals are poisons that kill pests. But why spend so much time and money killing pests?

Pests can do an enormous amount of damage to crops. It has been estimated that a third of the world's food production is destroyed by pests. The crops can be damaged at any of a number of stages – as seeds in the soil, as young plants or even after the crop has been harvested. To protect their crops from pest damage, farmers use chemical poisons called **pesticides**.

War on pests

There are several groups of pests – and often thousands of pests within each group.

Herbicides are chemicals that kill weeds – they are also known as weedkillers. If weeds were allowed to grow they would take away root space, soil nutrients and sunlight from the growing crops.

Fungicides kill tiny organisms called fungi. These organisms grown on the surface of seeds, plants or harvested crops.

Insecticides are used to kill insect pests that eat crops. DDT, dieldrin and pyrethrin are three examples. These are often sprayed over large fields by using special small aeroplanes.

Rodenticides are used to poison rodents such as rats and mice. These pests feed on stored grain and other crops. Warfarin is a common rodenticide – it causes death by internal bleeding.

Poor growth due to attack by soil pests shows which plants were not treated by pesticide.

After harvesting, weevil insects eat into crops such as barley.

Careful storage of crops is necessary to prevent pests from ruining food.

1
  a What is meant by the terms *rodenticide* and *insecticide*?
  b Give one example of each.

2 Name a pesticide that is sometimes an air pollutant. How does it get to pollute the air?

3
  a How many breeding pairs of peregrines disappeared from non-farming areas between 1940 and 1960?
  b How many disappeared from farming areas over the same period?
  c Explain why there was a difference in the two areas.

4 If one pigeon did not contain enough poison to kill a peregrine, explain why the bird of prey was still at risk.

5 One of the pesticides described will be no use in protecting harvested crops. Which one is it? Explain your answer.

Smoking isn't glamorous – it's expensive, smelly and dangerous.

Out of sight, but in your body

You can immediately notice some pollutants such as oil slicks, waste heaps and smoke from chimneys. But when you pollute your body you often can't see the harm being done. It can be a long time before you recognise the effect a pollutant is having on your health. By then it is often too late to do anything about it.

It is bad enough for people to suffer from pollution – but some people **choose** to add to this by 'polluting' their bodies through smoking.

What's in a cigarette?

Tobacco in cigarettes contains over 400 different chemicals. The most harmful of these are nicotine and tar. The amount of nicotine and tar in a cigarette depends on the type and brand. Government figures show that one cigarette may contain as much as 25 mg of tar and 2.5 mg of nicotine. When tobacco is burnt, it also produces a very poisonous gas called carbon monoxide – the same gas that is produced by burning petrol in cars!

No wonder smokers cough.

The tar and discharge that collects in the lungs of an average smoker.

Smoking 20 cigarettes a day means filling your lungs with up to 200cm^3 of tar each year.

Smoking can kill you...

Cigarette smoke is made up of sooty particles and tar. As smoke is inhaled, the tar gets trapped in the lungs. Tar damages the lungs by blocking them up. This leads to breathing disorders such as **lung cancer** and bronchitis. The number of deaths from lung cancer increases as more cigarettes are smoked. The chemicals which cause lung cancer are contained in the tar.

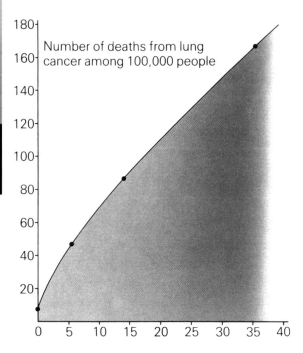

Number of deaths from lung cancer among 100,000 people

Number of cigarettes smoked every day

Smoke more, die sooner!

...in more ways than one.

When smoke is inhaled, carbon monoxide and nicotine from the smoke dissolve in the blood in the lungs.

Nicotine is the chemical which makes smokers become addicted to cigarettes. This means that they find it very hard to stop smoking.

Carbon monoxide takes the place of oxygen in the blood and makes smokers short of breath. Carbon monoxide also weakens the heart.

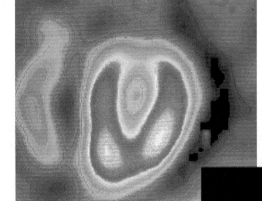

Healthy heart muscle shows up red in this scan. Which is the smoker and which is the non-smoker?

Many smokers die of heart attacks because the carbon monoxide has slowly killed off their heart muscles. It affects the heart most of all for the simple reason that this is the first organ to be supplied with blood from the lungs. Even after giving up smoking, smokers need plenty of exercise to strengthen their hearts again.

By smoking, you can kill others

A smoker 'actively' smokes a cigarette. A nearby non-smoker will also breathe in the smoke but from the air – not direct from the cigarette. The non-smoker is said to be a **passive smoker**.

This may happen regularly to a non-smoker. For example, when smokers and non-smokers share a house or workplace. In these cases, the non-smoker risks suffering from a smoking-related illness – even though he or she may have never smoked a cigarette.

Regular passive smoking makes non-smokers 30% more likely to get lung cancer.

1 How many different chemicals are found in a cigarette?

2
  a If you smoked 20 cigarettes a day for one year, how much nicotine would you inhale?
  b How much money would it have cost you?

3 How many people died from lung cancer who were:
  a non-smokers;
  b 20 cigarettes a day smokers?

4
  a What chemical in a cigarette causes lung cancer?
  b What chemical makes smokers short of breath and causes heart disease.

5 Why do smokers find it very hard to stop smoking?

6 Do you think smoking should be banned in all public places? Give reasons for your answer.

2.12 Noise pollution

What a racket!

If you've ever been to pop concert or disco you'll know it can be an enjoyable but noisy experience. You may agree that some kinds of music are rubbish – but would you think of it as pollution? While touring in Germany in 1986, a British group was reported to have caused a small earthquake. How about that for affecting the environment?.

Sound is a form of energy but when it becomes so loud that it can harm you, it is called **noise**. Noise can be thought of as a form of pollution because it can damage your body.

'Heavy metal' can mean noise pollution as well as chemical pollution!

Where does it come from?

Life in towns is generally very noisy. How often do you get to hear complete silence? Not very often, there is always some noise to be heard.

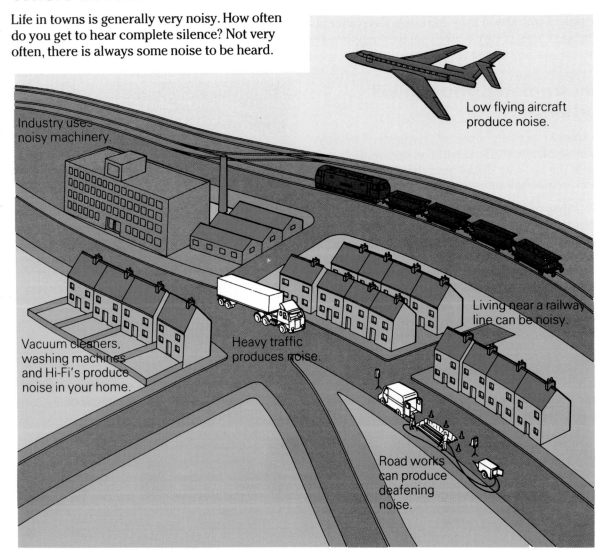

Industry uses noisy machinery.

Low flying aircraft produce noise.

Living near a railway line can be noisy.

Vacuum cleaners, washing machines and Hi-Fi's produce noise in your home.

Heavy traffic produces noise.

Road works can produce deafening noise.

How loud is loud?

The amount of energy or the level of noise is measure in **decibels** (dB). It is measured by sound level meters. If one noise is twice as loud as another, the noise level increases by 10 dB.

So a vacuum cleaner making a noise of 70 dB is twice as loud as a normal conversation. Likewise, 120 dB from a low jet is twice as loud as a 110 dB road drill. The sound of an explosion may even have enough energy to break glass.

	Type of Noise	Noise Level (dB)
	Conversation	60
	Door slamming	80
	Road drill	110
	Whisper	20
	Vacuum cleaner	70
	Low flying jet	120

Over the top

Constant exposure to noise levels greater than 80 dB may cause permanent loss of hearing. This can mean you will not hear quiet sounds and somebody else's speech may sound confused.

Many people like to use personal stereos to listen to music. These can damage your hearing if they are too loud. If a person at an arm's length away has to shout before you can hear them, then the sound is too noisy for your own good.

Reduce the sound level or you'll 'reduce' your hearing!

Keeping it down

To reduce the level of noise, you have to use materials which will **absorb** the sound and not reflect it. This is called **sound-proofing**. In your home, there are materials such as carpets and curtains which will act as sound absorbers. In factories, noise levels have been reduced by supplying ear mufflers and using sound-absorbing screens.

By changing the material from which a machine is made you can also reduce the noise it makes. For example, using bronze gear wheels to replace much noisier steel ones in machinery. By using plastic parts even road-work drills can be made quieter!

Ear mufflers protect this worker from the damaging noise of this tree stripper.

1 Name two possible sources of noise pollution.

 2 Look at the table of noise levels.
  a What units are used to measure noise levels?
  b Which noise is the loudest?
  c Which noise is twice as loud as a vacuum cleaner?

 3 **a** Name two jobs where workers could be exposed to more than 80dB of noise.
  b What harm could happen to these workers?

 4 **a** Explain how screens can reduce noise levels in factories.
  b What type of material could they be made from?

5 What precautions should be taken to protect the hearing of a jet pilot?

A load of rubbish

In Britain, about 25 million tonnes of rubbish are produced each year. Apart from the huge mass involved, the volume of the rubbish presents problems too. And some of it is dangerous and poisonous as well!

This makes the problem of disposing of it very difficult. Local councils are responsible for waste disposal and have to find answers to these problems.

Contents of waste	1930	1980
Dust/cinders	55%	10%
Vegetables	10%	25%
Paper	15%	30%
Metal	5%	10%
Glass	2%	8%
Plastic	0%	10%
Other	13%	4%

There is much more rubbish nowadays and the type of rubbish has changed too.

Landfilling

Rubbish is usually buried and left to rot under large areas of land. At first, the rotting rubbish is smelly and can produce methane, a gas which burns. Once the rubbish has rotted, the land slowly settles back to its previous level. After some years, the land can then be used again.

But many plastics do not rot away. Land that is filled with this kind of rubbish does not settle very quickly. To help overcome this problem, the rubbish is sometimes **shredded** to small bits. These are **compressed** into bails and then buried. The land used to bury bails settles quickly and can be used again after only a few years.

Large holes have to be dug to bury everybody's rubbish.

Making use of rubbish

Some councils have developed more useful ways of disposing of rubbish. It is **incinerated** (burned) in a furnace at high temperature. In some places, the energy released is used to heat homes, greenhouses or even to drive electrical generators.

The remaining materials are **separated** into ash and metal. Councils can then sell this metal to help repay the cost of the incinerator and other equipment. The ash is easily buried and does not take up the same amount of space as the original rubbish.

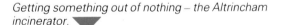

Getting something out of nothing – the Altrincham incinerator. ▼

Don't make a mess!

Most councils solve their rubbish problems by landfilling. This often seems the easiest and cheapest way, but it can pollute the environment.

Animal and plant habitats are destroyed when the ground is opened up for landfilling. Chemicals from the rubbish can seap out into streams and ponds for many years afterwards. During the landfilling, people cannot make any use of the area.

Many councils are aware of these problems and the dumping of dangerous rubbish is strictly controlled.

Careful disposal of rubbish means land fill sites can be safe to use in the future.

High-cost rubbish

The cost of new methods such as shredding, incinerating and separating is very high. The machines used to do the work may cost the community a lot of money. But this should be balanced against the cost to the environment. If rubbish is properly treated before disposal, the environment will not be in danger.

In some places, landfill sites are used for building new houses. If the landfilling was carried out safely, there should be no problems. But in the past, there have been places where the land had not been allowed to settle properly. Before long, the new houses needed expensive repairs – to mend the damage caused by bad landfillings.

Method	Cost	Speed	Risks
Landfill	£3 (per tonne)	very slow	seepage, landslips
Shredding and landfill	£7 (per tonne)	slow	seepage
Incinerating and separating	£15 (per tonne)	very fast	pollution from waste gases

---

1
  a Which type of rubbish was not present in 1930?
  b Which type has decreased the most since 1930? Give a reason to explain this decline.

2
What is the most common way that councils get rid of rubbish?

3
  a What sort of rubbish needs shredding?
  b How does shredding rubbish help in its disposal?

4
What are the advantages and disadvantages of using an incinerator to get rid of waste?

5
Would you mind living in a house built on an old landfill site? Explain the reasons for your answer.

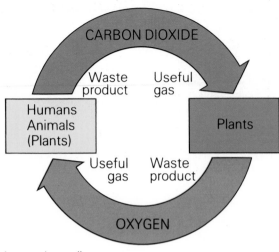

A natural recycling process

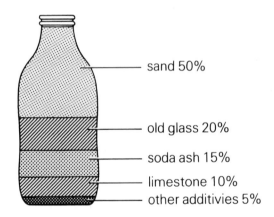

- sand 50%
- old glass 20%
- soda ash 15%
- limestone 10%
- other additivies 5%

Turning sand into new glass needs a lot of heat. Recycling old glass uses less heat.

Natural cycles

Your body produces waste carbon dioxide gas which you get rid of by breathing out. This gas is used by plants to help them live. Similarly, oxygen is produced as a waste gas by plants – but you need it to stay alive. The use and re-use of different materials between animals and plants is a **natural cycle** – a way of sharing the resources of the environment.

Metal cans, glass bottles and paper often end up as waste. A lot of energy and resources are needed to make these items and often they are just thrown away as rubbish. Not only is there waste, but often pollution too! More energy and more resources have to be used *just to replace* these items. No cycle here – just waste, waste and still more waste!

Recycling our rubbish

About a third of all our rubbish is made up of packaging that comes from metal, paper and glass. If all this packaging was not put in the dustbin, £50 000 000 a year could be cut from the national waste disposal bill.

If these materials could be **recycled** (used again), then even more money could be saved by reducing the amount of energy and resources needed to make replacement packaging.

During the Second World War, many things were in short supply – and recycling was commonplace. After the War, people wanted more convenience. There was plenty of resources and so rubbish was just thrown away. But nowadays things are being recycled – to save money and to protect the environment.

'Gotta lotta bottles'

Glass bottle manufacturers have developed a scheme where used bottles can be returned. People can throw their used bottles into a **bottle bank**. This glass is then used to make new bottles at a lower cost. All the manufacturers have to do is to melt down the old glass. The use of old glass to make new glass saves energy, helps to keep down the cost of new bottles. The local council usually sets up the bottle bank and gets paid by the manufacturers for the glass collected.

The 'cash a can' scheme

About 100 000 tonnes of expensive aluminium metal is thrown away each year. A recycling scheme has been set up to reduce this cost. Many schools make money out of this scheme by collecting old cans or 'ring tops'. This metal is then sold back to the manufacturers and the money used to help the school.

Iron and steel are often recycled in a similar way. The only problem is that large amounts of iron are difficult to collect and return. Some councils use special separating machines to collect these metals from their waste.

Making aluminium needs a lot of electricity. Recycling it helps to reduce costs – and reduces acid rain too!

Paper money

Nearly one million tonnes of paper are used each year. Making paper not only uses up important resources (trees), but also needs a lot of energy and releases a lot of pollution. Many organisations collect paper to raise money. The paper is then sold back to manufacturers, where it is recycled. The waste paper is then simply mixed with water, made into **pulp** and cleaned. After that it is ready for re-use.

Plastic pollution

Plastic materials are used more and more instead of paper packaging. But they do not rot away as easily as paper. Some new plastic materials are **biodegradable** – this means they will be decomposed by natural factors present in the environment.

Some biodegradable plastics will decompose when attacked by small organisms such as fungi (mould). Other biodegradable plastics are weakened by prolonged sunlight before breaking up into small pieces. These pieces are then completely decomposed by the action of fungi, small insects and other organisms involved in the rotting process.

Friends of the Earth Trust Ltd.

Recycling

The world cannot afford the luxury of a throw-away society. We need to reduce waste and conserve materials through re-use, repair and recycling.

Tree-saver! Look for this emblem on the back of recycled paper.

1 Give an example of how materials can be used and re-used in a natural cycle.

2 Give three examples of materials which can be recycled.

3 Explain in detail one scheme which recycles materials.

4 More and more plastic is used instead of paper
   a Explain carefully why this may be a problem
   b How it can be overcome?

5 What are the advantages and disadvantages recycling materials like metal, glass or paper?

2.15 The problem with pollution

There is a price to pay for our standard of living. Electricity is very convenient but power stations can produce acid rain. Cheap food is nice but the fertilisers and pesticides which are used to grow it slowly poison the environment.

Sometimes it is difficult to please everyone. Look at the problems facing the people who live on this island...

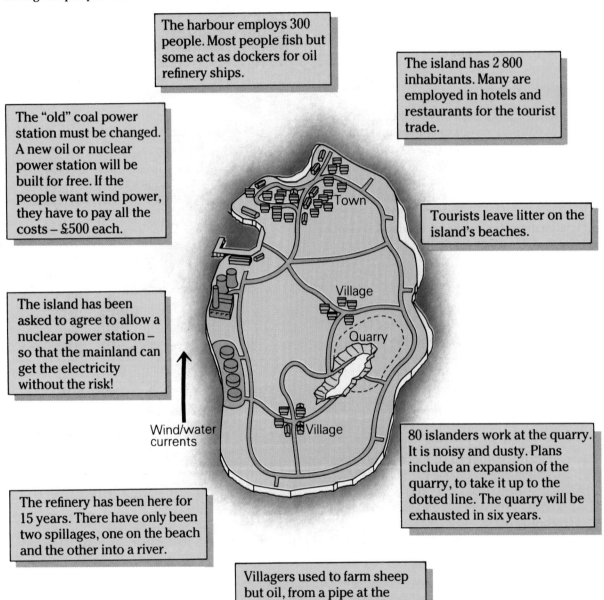

The harbour employs 300 people. Most people fish but some act as dockers for oil refinery ships.

The island has 2 800 inhabitants. Many are employed in hotels and restaurants for the tourist trade.

The "old" coal power station must be changed. A new oil or nuclear power station will be built for free. If the people want wind power, they have to pay all the costs – £500 each.

Tourists leave litter on the island's beaches.

The island has been asked to agree to allow a nuclear power station – so that the mainland can get the electricity without the risk!

The refinery has been here for 15 years. There have only been two spillages, one on the beach and the other into a river.

80 islanders work at the quarry. It is noisy and dusty. Plans include an expansion of the quarry, to take it up to the dotted line. The quarry will be exhausted in six years.

Villagers used to farm sheep but oil, from a pipe at the refinery, polluted the river and ruined their grazing land.

Town

Village

Quarry

Village

Wind/water currents

More information about the island is on the next page. Find out more about the island and what is happening there and then try to answer some of the questions.

THE ISLAND NEWS

Beach disaster

Another oil slick threatens to ruin the holiday trade for the coming year. Hotelier Emma Lowe said 'Last year the beaches were a mess and next year we will lose even more business.' Local Councillor Anita Forster said that it was time that the refinery paid for its mistakes.

In an interview with the manager of the refinery he said that little could be done to stop small amounts of oil from seeping out. They would be mounting an inquiry into the matter as soon as possible. Until then, some new methods of stopping the oil from spreading were being tried.

Farm finishes

Another farm in the hills has closed as more people leave the island for work on the mainland. Some people may be able to get jobs with the Quarry Company if it is allowed to expand the scale of its mining works.

Local M.P. and councillors meet

Charles Hutton the newly elected Member of Parliament, will meet councillors to discuss the island's future. Islanders are asked to attend the meeting tonight to voice their concern over a wide range of issues. In a recent TV discussion, the M.P. indicated his worry that tourism on the islands had taken a sharp decline since more and more industries had been set up on the islands.

Record fishing catch

Young fisherman Mike and his wife Bethan have hauled in a record catch. Their new boat run by their family went out into deep waters to get their fish. Young fisherwoman, Bethan said that it was very hard work but they had to leave the polluted waters close to the island to find the fish. In recent years the size of their catch has dropped to less than half it was 5 years ago.

---

1 Identify as many as you can of the sources of pollution which are already on the island.

2 Which pollution risks may be added to these in the future?

3 Which industries benefit the community?

4 If you attend the meeting with the M.P. and the councillors, what would you have to say?

MODULE 2 POLLUTION

Index (refers to spread numbers)

Photo Acknowledgements

The references indicate the spread number and, where appropriate, the photo sequence.

Altrincham Council 2.13/2; J Allan Cash *2.1/5, 2.8/1, 2.12/1, 2.15/3;* Friends of the Earth *2.14/2;* Geo Science Features 2.2, *2.7/2, 2.11/1;* Sally & Richard Greenhill *2.11/5, 2.12/2;* Greenpeace *(Kalvert) 2.1/3, (Zindler) 2.1/4, (Venneman) 2.3/3, (Gleizes) 2.9;* Health Education Authority *2.11/2;* John Hillelson Agency *2.8/2;* Holt Studios *2.1/7, 2.6/2, 2.10/2, 2.10/3, 2.12/3;* E & D Hosking – *Contents, 2.1/2, 2.7/1, 2.10/1, 2.13/1, 2.15/1;* Impact Photos *2.3/1, 2.3/2;* ICCE (C Agen) 2.3/4, (M Boulton) 2.13/3, (M Hogget) 2.14/1, (P Steele) *2.14/2;* Frank Lane Agency *(J Lynch) 2.1/1, (S Malowski) 2.10/4;* Panos Pictures *(G Castro) 2.5, 2.6/1;* Chris Ridgers *2.15/2;* Science Photo Library *2.1/6, 2.4, 2.11/3, 2.11/4.*

Picture Research: Jennifer Johnson

Trevor Senior

ESSENTIALS
AQA
GCSE Maths
Higher Tier
Revision Guide

Contents

Contents

		Maths A Unit Reference	Revised

Rounding

Rounding and Approximation

Numbers are **rounded**:
- to **estimate** the value of a calculation using **approximations**.
- to give a sensible answer.

Example

Jack sees batteries advertised for £1.49 each. He has £10. How many can he buy?

Solution

Problem Solving
Use a sensible estimate to make this type of calculation easier.

Using £1.50 he would get 2 for £3, so he can buy 6 for £9. He doesn't have enough left to buy any more.

Estimating Values of Calculations

When you approximate the value of a number always work to 1 **significant figure** (see page 5). For example, 18.8 approximates to 20 using 1 significant figure.

Example 1

Use approximations to estimate the value of:

$$\frac{5020}{4.9 \times 20.8}$$

Solution

5020 = 5000 to 1 significant figure

4.9 = 5 to 1 significant figure

20.8 = 20 to 1 significant figure

$$\frac{5000}{5 \times 20} = 50$$

Example 2

Use approximations to estimate the value of:

$$\frac{19.7 \times 30.1}{0.59}$$

Solution

Rounding each number to 1 significant figure

$\frac{19.7 \times 30.1}{0.59}$ is approximately $\frac{20 \times 30}{0.6}$

$$\frac{20 \times 30}{0.6} = \frac{600}{0.6}$$

To remove the decimal from this calculation, multiply the numerator and denominator by 10

$$= \frac{6000}{6} = 1000$$

So $\frac{19.7 \times 30.1}{0.59}$ is approximately 1000

Key Words   **Rounding • Estimate • Approximation • Significant figure**

Decimal Places

Look at the number **27.35083**

To round to 1 **decimal place**, look at the **second** decimal place:

- If the second decimal place has a value of 5 or more, round up the number in the first decimal place.
- If the second decimal place has a value of less than 5, leave the number in the first decimal place unchanged.

To round to **2 decimal places**, look at the **third** decimal place, and so on.

So:

- $27.3 \,|\, \mathbf{5}083 = 27.4$ to 1 decimal place (i.e. 3 rounds up to 4)
- $27.35 \,|\, \mathbf{0}83 = 27.35$ to 2 decimal places (i.e. 5 stays unchanged)
- $27.350 \,|\, \mathbf{8}3 = 27.351$ to 3 decimal places (i.e. 0 rounds up to 1).

Significant Figures

The first **significant figure** is the first non-zero digit from the left.

Look again at the number **27.35083**

To round to 1 significant figure, look at the **second** significant figure:

- If the second significant figure has a value of 5 or more, round up the first significant figure.
- If the second significant figure has a value of less than 5, leave the first significant figure unchanged.

To round to **2 significant figures**, look at the **third** significant figure, and so on.

Use zeros to keep the place value of the significant figures.

So:

- $2 \,|\, \mathbf{7}.35083 = 30$ to 1 significant figure (i.e. 2 rounds up to 3 and put a zero in the units column)
- $27. \,|\, \mathbf{3}5083 = 27$ to 2 significant figures (i.e. 7 stays unchanged)
- $27.3 \,|\, \mathbf{5}083 = 27.4$ to 3 significant figures (i.e. 3 rounds up to 4).

Example

Write the number 0.03053 to 2 significant figures.

Solution

The first significant figure is the digit 3.

So $0.030 \,|\, \mathbf{5}3 = 0.031$ to 2 significant figures.

> 0 is followed by a 5, so round up to 1

> The leading zeros are used to keep the place value of the significant figures

Quick Test

1. Round the following numbers to:
   - **i)** 1 decimal place
   - **ii)** 2 decimal places
   - **iii)** 1 significant figure
   - **iv)** 2 significant figures.
   - **a)** 18.725 **b)** 0.0725 **c)** 2436.518

2. Use approximations to estimate the value of each of the following:
   - **a)** $\dfrac{71.2 + 28.8}{9.5}$
   - **b)** $\dfrac{4.15 \times 38.7}{7.69}$
   - **c)** $\dfrac{99.9 \times 5.87}{0.29}$

Multiples and Factors

Order of Operations

BIDMAS is a way of remembering the order to carry out operations. Simplify **brackets** first, then work out any **indices** (powers) and finally **divide, multiply, add** and **subtract** in that order:

- **B**rackets, e.g. $2 \times (8 + 3) = 2 \times 11 = 22$
- **I**ndices (or powers), e.g. $3^2 \times (7 - 2)^2 = 3^2 \times 5^2$
  $= 9 \times 25 = 225$
- **D**ivision, e.g. $3 + 4^2 \div 2 = 3 + 16 \div 2 = 3 + 8 = 11$
- **M**ultiplication, e.g. $3 \times 8 \div 2 + 1$
  $= 3 \times 4 + 1 = 12 + 1 = 13$
- **A**ddition, e.g. $3 + 5 \times 4^2 = 3 + 5 \times 16$
  $= 3 + 80 = 83$
- **S**ubtraction, e.g. $3 \times 10 \div 2 - 1 + 4$
  $= 3 \times 5 - 1 + 4 = 15 - 1 + 4 = 18$

Number Facts

You should know these sets of numbers:
- **Even numbers**: 2, 4, 6, 8, 10…
- **Odd numbers**: 1, 3, 5, 7, 9…
- **Prime numbers**: 2, 3, 5, 7, 11…

Multiples of a number are found by multiplying the number by another **integer**. For example:
- multiples of 3 are 3, 6, 9, 12, 15…
- multiples of 7 are 7, 14, 21, 28, 35…

Factors of a number are all the whole numbers that divide into it exactly. For example:
- factors of 17 are 1 and 17
- factors of 18 are 1, 2, 3, 6, 9 and 18
- factors of 25 are 1, 5 and 25.

N.B. Prime numbers only have two factors – the number itself and 1.

Product of Prime Factors

Prime factors are factors of a number that are also prime.

Example

Write 24 as a **product** of prime factors.

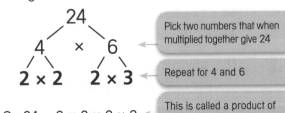

Solution A

Using a factor tree:

Pick two numbers that when multiplied together give 24

Repeat for 4 and 6

So $24 = 2 \times 2 \times 2 \times 3$

This is called a product of prime factors

$= 2^3 \times 3$

Product of prime factors in **index form**

Solution B

Using prime factor decomposition:

2	24
2	12
2	6
3	3
	1

2 is prime and is a factor of 24, so $24 \div 2 = 12$

2 is also a factor of 12, so $12 \div 2 = 6$

2 is also a factor of 6, so $6 \div 2 = 3$

3 is prime and is a factor of itself, so $3 \div 3 = 1$

So $24 = 2 \times 2 \times 2 \times 3$

$= 2^3 \times 3$

Key Words   BIDMAS • Even number • Odd number • Prime number • Multiple • Integer • Factor

Least Common Multiple and Highest Common Factor

Least Common Multiple (LCM)

The **least common multiple** (or lowest common multiple) of two numbers is the lowest number that is in the multiplication tables of both numbers.

Example 1

Work out the least common multiple of 5 and 8.

Solution

Multiples of 5 are:

5, 10, 15, 20, 25, 30, 35, (40), 45…

Multiples of 8 are:

8, 16, 24, 32, (40), 48, 56…

40 is the lowest number in both lists, so 40 is the least common multiple.

Example 2

Work out the highest common factor of 24 and 40.

Solution

The factors of 24 are:

1, 2, 3, 4, 6, (8), 12 and 24.

The factors of 40 are:

1, 2, 4, 5, (8), 10, 20 and 40.

8 is the highest number in both lists, so 8 is the highest common factor.

Highest Common Factor (HCF)

The **highest common factor** of two numbers is the highest number that divides into both numbers.

Example 3

The least common multiple of two numbers is 24. The highest common factor of the same two numbers is 4.

Work out the two numbers.

Solution

Problem Solving

Break this type of question into several steps. Start by listing the multiples of 4 as you know that 4 is a factor of both numbers.

Multiples of 4 are 4, 8, 12, 16, 20, 24…

Numbers in this list which are factors of 24 are 8, 12 and 24.

The two numbers must be 8 and 12 to satisfy both conditions.

Quick Test

1. Work out the following:
   a) $(6 - 4) \times (5 + 2)$ b) $5^3 + 50 \div 10$ c) $3^2 + 4^2 + 5^2 \times 2$
2. Write 60 as a product of prime factors. Give your answer in index form.
3. Work out the least common multiple of the following:
   a) 8 and 10   b) 4 and 7   c) 6 and 9
4. Work out the highest common factor of the following:
   a) 20 and 28   b) 15 and 25   c) 12 and 30

Key Words   Prime factor • Product • Least common multiple • Highest common factor

Fractions

Equivalent Fractions

Equivalent fractions are fractions that can be simplified (cancelled down) to the same value.

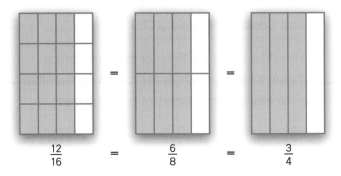

$$\frac{12}{16} = \frac{6}{8} = \frac{3}{4}$$

Adding and Subtracting Fractions

To add or subtract fractions they must have the same **denominator**.

Example 1

Work out $2\frac{2}{3} + 1\frac{1}{2}$

Solution

$2\frac{2}{3} + 1\frac{1}{2} = 2 + 1 + \frac{2}{3} + \frac{1}{2}$

$= 3 + \frac{4}{6} + \frac{3}{6}$ ← $= 3 + \frac{7}{6}$

$= 3 + 1\frac{1}{6}$

$= 4\frac{1}{6}$

Example 2

Work out $4\frac{1}{4} - 2\frac{1}{2}$

Solution A

$4\frac{1}{4} - 2\frac{1}{2} = 4 - 2 + \frac{1}{4} - \frac{1}{2}$

$= 2 - \frac{1}{4} = 1\frac{3}{4}$

Solution B

$4\frac{1}{4} - 2\frac{1}{2} = \frac{17}{4} - \frac{5}{2}$ ← Here we are changing the mixed numbers to improper fractions

$= \frac{17}{4} - \frac{10}{4}$

$= \frac{7}{4}$

$= 1\frac{3}{4}$

Multiplying Fractions

To multiply fractions:
1. change any **mixed numbers** to **improper fractions**
2. multiply the **numerators** together
3. multiply the denominators together
4. simplify the answer if possible.

Example 1

Work out $\frac{3}{4} \times \frac{3}{5}$

Solution

$\frac{3}{4} \times \frac{3}{5} = \frac{9}{20}$

Example 2

Work out $2\frac{2}{3} \times 1\frac{1}{5}$

Solution

$2\frac{2}{3} \times 1\frac{1}{5} = \frac{8}{3} \times \frac{6}{5}$

$= \frac{8}{3^1} \times \frac{6^2}{5}$ ← Simplify by cancelling by 3

$= \frac{16}{5}$

$= 3\frac{1}{5}$

Dividing Fractions

To divide fractions:

1. change any mixed numbers to improper fractions
2. turn the second fraction upside down and change the division to multiplication
3. do the multiplication as shown on page 8.

Example 1

Work out $\frac{5}{6} \div \frac{3}{5}$

Solution

$$\frac{5}{6} \div \frac{3}{5} = \frac{5}{6} \times \frac{5}{3}$$

$$= \frac{25}{18}$$

$$= 1\frac{7}{18}$$

Example 2

Work out $1\frac{1}{4} \div 2\frac{1}{3}$

Solution

$$1\frac{1}{4} \div 2\frac{1}{3} = \frac{5}{4} \div \frac{7}{3}$$

$$= \frac{5}{4} \times \frac{3}{7}$$

$$= \frac{15}{28}$$

Fractions of Quantities

To calculate a fraction of a quantity, multiply the fraction by the quantity.

To write a quantity as a fraction of another quantity:

1. match the units
2. write the fraction and simplify.

Example 1

$\frac{3}{4}$ of the 28 students in a class are boys. How many are girls?

Solution

> **Problem Solving**
>
> You can either work out $\frac{1}{4}$ of 28 for the number of girls or $\frac{3}{4}$ of 28 for the number of boys and then subtract this from the total number of students.

$$\frac{3}{4} \text{ of } 28 = \frac{3}{4} \times 28$$

$$= \frac{3}{\cancel{4}^{1}} \times \frac{\cancel{28}^{7}}{1} = 21$$

There are 21 boys, so there are:

$$28 - 21 = 7 \text{ girls}$$

Example 2

Write 30 cm as a fraction of 1 metre.

Solution

1 metre = 100 cm ← Make the units the same

So 30 cm as a fraction of 1 metre is $\frac{30 \text{ cm}}{100 \text{ cm}} = \frac{3}{10}$

Example 3

In two tests, Nicholas gets 13 out of 15 and 16 out of 20.

Which is the better score?

Solution

> **Problem Solving**
>
> To compare the two scores, one way is to write them as fractions with common denominators. Then compare the numerators.

13 out of 15 is $\frac{13}{15} = \frac{52}{60}$ ← Multiply the numerator and denominator by 4

16 out of 20 is $\frac{16}{20} = \frac{48}{60}$ ← Multiply the numerator and denominator by 3

So 13 out of 15 is the better score.

Quick Test

1. Work out the following:

   a) $1\frac{1}{4} + 3\frac{1}{3}$ b) $2\frac{3}{5} - 1\frac{1}{4}$ c) $1\frac{1}{2} \times 1\frac{1}{3}$ d) $3\frac{4}{5} \div 2\frac{1}{6}$

2. Work out $\frac{2}{3}$ of £60.

3. Write 50 grams as a fraction of 1 kilogram. (*Hint: 1 kg = 1000 g*)

Percentages

Calculating a Percentage of a Quantity

To calculate a **percentage** of a **quantity**:

1. change the percentage to a fraction or a decimal fraction
2. calculate the fraction of the quantity.

Example

Work out 80% of 200 grams.

Solution

80% of 200 grams is $\frac{80}{100} \times 200 = 160$ grams

One Quantity as a Percentage of Another Quantity

To express one quantity as a percentage of another quantity:

1. make sure both quantities are in the same units
2. express the quantity as a fraction of the other quantity
3. change the fraction to a percentage.

Example

Express 50p as a percentage of £2.

Solution

50p as a percentage of 200p $= \frac{50}{200} \times 100 = 25\%$

Increasing or Decreasing Quantities by a Percentage

To increase or decrease a quantity by a percentage:

- work out the increase and add it on
- work out the decrease and subtract it.

Alternatively:

- write down the **multiplier**
- multiply the original amount by the multiplier.

Example 1

Jo's pay is £17 000 per year. She gets a 5% pay rise. Work out her new pay.

Solution A

5% of £17 000

$= \frac{5}{100} \times 17\,000$

$= £850$

New pay is 17 000 + 850 = £17 850

Solution B (Multiplier method)

5% extra is the same as 100% + 5% = 105%

$105\% = \frac{105}{100} = 1.05$ ← The decimal equivalent is called the **multiplier**

105% of £17 000

$= 1.05 \times 17\,000$

$= £17\,850$

Example 2

Which offer is better value?

Offer 1

Offer 2

Solution

> **Problem Solving**
>
> When asked which is the 'better value' always work out the cost for the same quantity so that you can compare.

Offer 1 = 1000 g for £2.25

Offer 2 = 750 g for £1.80

Offer 1 would cost $\frac{£2.25}{4} = 56.25$p ← Work out the cost of 250 g

Offer 2 would cost $\frac{£1.80}{3} = 60$p

So Offer 1 is better value.

Percentage Change

To work out **percentage change**:

1. work out the change, e.g. increase, decrease, profit or loss
2. use the formula shown.

$$\text{Percentage change} = \frac{\text{change}}{\text{original amount}} \times 100\%$$

Example

Mr Smith bought a ring for £250 and sold it for £400. Work out his percentage profit.

Solution

$$\text{Percentage profit} = \frac{\text{profit}}{\text{original amount}} \times 100\%$$

$$= \frac{150}{250} \times 100$$

Profit is £400 − £250 = £150

$$= 60\%$$

Compound and Reverse Percentages

Compound Percentages

A **compound percentage** is a repeated percentage calculation.

Example

£2000 is invested at 5% per annum compound interest. Work out the value after 2 years.

Solution A

5% of £2000 is £100

So after 1 year the investment is worth £2100

5% of £2100 is £105

So after 2 years the investment is worth £2205.

Solution B (Multiplier method)

5% gives a multiplier of 1.05

So after 2 years the investment is worth:

$$2000 \times 1.05 \times 1.05 = £2205$$

Reverse Percentages

Reverse percentage involves working backwards from the **final amount** to the **original amount**.

Example

Work out the original price of the TV.

20% OFF
SALE PRICE: £496

Solution

20% off means it is 100% − 20% = 80% of the original price.

So 80% is £496

1% is $\frac{496}{80}$

Original price (100%) is:

$$\frac{496}{80} \times 100 = £620$$

Quick Test

1. Work out 30% of 600 grams.
2. Express 25 cm as a percentage of 3 metres.
3. **a)** Increase £14 by 20%   **b)** Decrease 120 minutes by 35%
4. Work out the value of £1000 invested for 3 years at 4% compound interest.
5. The number of workers in an office was reduced to 12. This is a 20% reduction. How many used to work in the office?

Key Words   Percentage change • Compound percentage • Reverse percentage

Powers and Roots

Square and Cube Numbers

You need to know all the **square numbers** up to $15^2 = 225$

$1^2 =$	$2^2 =$	$3^2 =$	$4^2 =$	$5^2 =$	$6^2 =$	$7^2 =$	$8^2 =$
1	**4**	**9**	**16**	**25**	**36**	**49**	**64**

$9^2 =$	$10^2 =$	$11^2 =$	$12^2 =$	$13^2 =$	$14^2 =$	$15^2 =$
81	**100**	**121**	**144**	**169**	**196**	**225**

You need to know the following **cube numbers**:

$1^3 =$	$2^3 =$	$3^3 =$	$4^3 =$	$5^3 =$	$10^3 =$
1	**8**	**27**	**64**	**125**	**1000**

You also need to know the corresponding **square roots** and **cube roots**, e.g. $\sqrt{121} = 11$ and $\sqrt[3]{64} = 4$. The square root of a number can be positive or negative, e.g. $\sqrt{49} = +7$ or -7

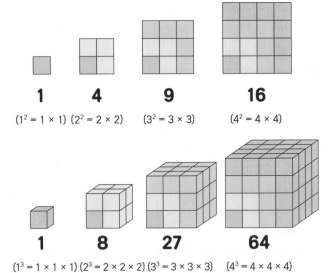

1 **4** **9** **16**
$(1^2 = 1 \times 1)$ $(2^2 = 2 \times 2)$ $(3^2 = 3 \times 3)$ $(4^2 = 4 \times 4)$

1 **8** **27** **64**
$(1^3 = 1 \times 1 \times 1)$ $(2^3 = 2 \times 2 \times 2)$ $(3^3 = 3 \times 3 \times 3)$ $(4^3 = 4 \times 4 \times 4)$

Working with Powers and Roots

The **power** or **index** (plural: indices) of a number is the number of times a number is multiplied by itself, e.g. $5^3 = 5 \times 5 \times 5$ and $2^4 = 2 \times 2 \times 2 \times 2$. You need to know that 10^6 is 1 million.

When working with indices, follow these rules:

* To multiply powers of the same number, add the indices.
  $3^4 \times 3^5 = 3^{(4+5)} = 3^9$
* To divide powers of the same number, subtract the indices.
  $6^7 \div 6^2 = 6^{(7-2)} = 6^5$
* To work out the power of a number to another power, multiply the indices.
  $(10^2)^3 = 10^6$ (1 million)
* Any number to the power 1 is itself.
  $8^1 = 8$
* Any number to the power zero is 1.
  $4^0 = 1$
* Any number to a **negative power** is the **reciprocal** of the same number to the positive power.
  $9^{-2} = \dfrac{1}{9^2} = \dfrac{1}{81}$

Make sure that you know how to work with powers and roots on your calculator.

For example:

Input	Keys	Display
24^2	(2) (4) (x^2) (=)	576
$\sqrt{289}$	($\sqrt{\blacksquare}$) (2) (8) (9) (=)	17
10^6	(1) (0) ($x^{\blacksquare}$) (6) (=)	1 000 000
5^{-1}	(5) (x^{-1}) (=)	0.2
$\sqrt[3]{90}$	(SHIFT) ($\sqrt[\sqrt[3]{\blacksquare}]{\blacksquare}$) (9) (0) (=)	4.481…

Your calculator may work differently to the examples above. Make sure you know how it works.

Rules of indices also work in algebra. For example:

* $x^4 \times x^5 = x^{(4+5)} = x^9$
* $x^7 \div x^2 = x^{(7-2)} = x^5$
* $(x^2)^3 = x^6$

Key Words   Square number • Cube number • Square root • Cube root • Power • Index

Example 1

a) Simplify $\dfrac{4^6 \times 4^2}{4^5}$

Solution

$$\dfrac{4^6 \times 4^2}{4^5} = \dfrac{4^8}{4^5} = 4^3$$

b) Work out the value of $\dfrac{3^2 \times 3^3}{3^7}$

Solution

$$\dfrac{3^2 \times 3^3}{3^7} = \dfrac{3^5}{3^7}$$
$$= 3^{-2}$$
$$= \dfrac{1}{3^2}$$
$$= \dfrac{1}{9}$$

Example 2

Which is greater, 5^0 or 5^{-2}?

Solution

Problem Solving
Use the rules of indices to work out the values and remember to say which is greater.

$5^0 = 1$

$5^{-2} = \dfrac{1}{5^2} = \dfrac{1}{25}$

1 is greater than $\frac{1}{25}$, so 5^0 is greater than 5^{-2}.

Fractional Powers (Roots)

A **fractional power** is a root:

- Power $\frac{1}{2}$ is the positive square root.

- Power $\frac{1}{3}$ is the cube root, and so on.

Example 1

Work out the value of:

a) $25^{\frac{1}{2}}$

Solution

$$25^{\frac{1}{2}} = \sqrt{25} = 5$$

b) $16^{\frac{1}{4}}$

Solution

$$16^{\frac{1}{4}} = \sqrt[4]{16} = 2$$

Because
$2 \times 2 \times 2 \times 2 = 16$

c) $8^{\frac{2}{3}}$

Solution

$$8^{\frac{2}{3}} = \left(\sqrt[3]{8}\right)^2 = 2^2 = 4$$

It's always easier to work out the root first

Example 2

Work out the value of:

a) $16^{-\frac{1}{4}}$

Solution

$$16^{-\frac{1}{4}} = \dfrac{1}{16^{\frac{1}{4}}} = \dfrac{1}{\sqrt[4]{16}} = \dfrac{1}{2}$$

b) $125^{-\frac{2}{3}}$

Solution

$$125^{-\frac{2}{3}} = \dfrac{1}{125^{\frac{2}{3}}} = \dfrac{1}{\left(\sqrt[3]{125}\right)^2} = \dfrac{1}{5^2} = \dfrac{1}{25}$$

Quick Test

1. Write down the value of:
   a) 12^2 **b)** 3^3
   c) $\sqrt{169}$ **d)** $\sqrt[3]{1000}$

2. Work out the values of:
   a) $36^{\frac{1}{2}}$ **b)** $125^{\frac{1}{3}}$
   c) $8^{-\frac{1}{3}}$ **d)** $27^{-\frac{2}{3}}$

Standard Index Form

Standard Form

Standard form or standard index form is a way of writing numbers using **powers of 10**. The number to be expressed in standard form is written as a number between 1 and 10 and multiplied by a power of 10:

$a \times 10^n$ where $1 \leqslant a < 10$ and n is a whole number

Remember these points about n:

- For **large** numbers n is **positive**.
- For **small** numbers (fractions less than 1) n is **negative**.
- The value of n tells you how many **places** the digits have moved.

Example 1

Write in standard form:

a) 24.3

Solution

$24.3 = 2.43 \times 10^1$ ← Digits have moved one place to the right

b) 6471

Solution

$6471 = 6.471 \times 10^3$ ← Digits have moved three places to the right

c) 500

Solution

$500 = 5 \times 10^2$ ← Digits have moved two places to the right

d) 0.048

Solution

$0.048 = 4.8 \times 10^{-2}$ ← Digits have moved two places to the left

e) 0.002

Solution

$0.002 = 2 \times 10^{-3}$ ← Digits have moved three places to the left

f) 9.61

Solution

$9.61 = 9.61 \times 10^0$ ← Digits haven't moved

Example 2

Write these numbers in order starting with the smallest:

$$1.6 \times 10^5 \qquad 2.5 \times 10^4 \qquad 2.1 \times 10^5$$

Solution

Problem Solving

When asked to order numbers in standard form, sort them by order of powers first – the higher the power, the bigger the value.

The middle number is the smallest as it has the lowest power.

The others have the same power but 1.6 is smaller than 2.1

So in order the numbers are:

$$2.5 \times 10^4 \qquad 1.6 \times 10^5 \qquad 2.1 \times 10^5$$

Calculations with Standard Form

Numbers in standard form can be keyed into a calculator. To enter the number 1.2×10^7 key in as shown.

The calculator will display the numbers either as an **ordinary number** or in standard form.

Or:

Adding or Subtracting Numbers Given in Standard Form

To add or subtract numbers given in standard form, write
them as ordinary numbers and then do the calculation.

Example

Work out:

a) $2.5 \times 10^3 + 8.9 \times 10^4$

Solution

$2.5 \times 10^3 + 8.9 \times 10^4 = 2500 + 89\,000$

$= 91\,500$ or 9.15×10^4

b) $2.3 \times 10^{-1} - 7.7 \times 10^{-2}$

Solution

$2.3 \times 10^{-1} - 7.7 \times 10^{-2} = 0.23 - 0.077$

$= 0.153$ or 1.53×10^{-1}

Multiplying or Dividing Numbers Given in Standard Form

To multiply or divide numbers given in standard form,
work out the numbers and the powers separately.
Check that the answer is in standard form.

Example

Work out:

a) $2.1 \times 10^3 \times 4 \times 10^4$

Solution

$2.1 \times 10^3 \times 4 \times 10^4$

$= (2.1 \times 4) \times (10^3 \times 10^4)$

$= 8.4 \times 10^7$ ← *Add the powers of 10*

b) $6.9 \times 10^3 \div 1.5 \times 10^{-3}$

Solution

$6.9 \times 10^3 \div 1.5 \times 10^{-3}$

$= (6.9 \div 1.5) \times (10^3 \div 10^{-3})$

$= 4.6 \times 10^6$ ← *Subtract the powers of 10*

c) $4.2 \times 10^3 \times 9.4 \times 10^2$

Solution

$4.2 \times 10^3 \times 9.4 \times 10^2$

$= (4.2 \times 9.4) \times (10^3 \times 10^2)$

$= 39.48 \times 10^5$ ← *Note that this isn't in standard form*

$= 3.948 \times 10^1 \times 10^5$

$= 3.948 \times 10^6$

Quick Test

1. Write these numbers in standard form:
   a) 372   **b)** 6000   **c)** 0.023   **d)** 5.67

2. Write these as ordinary numbers:
   a) 3.14×10^2 **b)** 2.1×10^4 **c)** 3.65×10^{-1} **d)** 5.8×10^{-2}

3. Work out:
   a) $3.6 \times 10^2 + 1.7 \times 10^3$ **b)** $8.1 \times 10^2 - 2.4 \times 10^3$ **c)** $3.9 \times 10^2 \times 6.2 \times 10^3$ **d)** $\dfrac{4 \times 10^6}{8 \times 10^9}$

Ratio

Simplifying a Ratio

A **ratio** (:) is used to compare two or
more quantities.

Example 1

Express 30 cm to 2 metres as a ratio in its simplest form.

Solution

30 cm : 2 metres = 30 cm : 200 cm ←

= 3 : 20

> When working with ratios, always use common units so they can cancel out

Example 2

The scale on a map is given as 1 cm to 2 km.
Express this as a ratio in its simplest form.

Solution

1 km = 1000 metres; 1 metre = 100 cm

So 2 km = 200 000 cm ← Change to a common unit

The ratio of the map is 1 cm : 200 000 cm

= 1 : 200 000 ← Cancel out the units

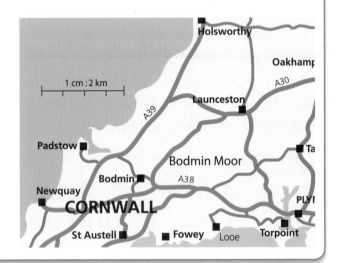

Ratios as Fractions

A ratio can be written as a fraction.

Example

Matthew and Natasha share a pizza in the ratio 3 : 2

What fraction does Matthew eat?

Solution

> **Problem Solving**
>
> Use the total number of parts in the ratio to represent the total number of pieces of pizza. Then write the number Matthew eats as a fraction of the total number of pieces.

The ratio has 5 parts altogether.

Matthew eats 3 out of the 5 pieces, so he eats $\frac{3}{5}$ of
the pizza.

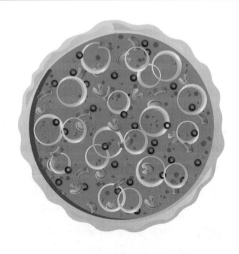

Dividing a Quantity in a Given Ratio

You can share quantities by using ratio. The parts in the ratio represent the proportions.

Example 1

An orange drink is made of orange juice and water in the ratio 1 : 4

How much water is used in a 200 ml drink?

Solution

There are 4 + 1 = 5 parts in the ratio altogether. So 5 parts is 200 ml.

1 part is 40 ml ◄— *Dividing by 5*

4 parts are 160 ml ◄— *Multiplying by 4*

So 160 ml of water is used.

Example 2

The ratio of adults to children at a football match is 7 : 3. There are 1500 children at the match. How many more adults are there than children?

Problem Solving

Always start by working out one part. Then work out how many more parts are for adults than children or work out the number of adults.

Solution A

Children represent 3 parts of the ratio.

So 3 parts = 1500

1 part = 500 ◄— *Dividing by 3*

Adults represent 4 more parts than children in the ratio.

So 4 parts = 2000 ◄— *Multiplying by 4*

There are 2000 more adults than children.

Solution B

Children represent 3 parts of the ratio.

So 3 parts = 1500

1 part = 500 ◄— *Dividing by 3*

Adults represent 7 parts.

So 7 parts = 3500 ◄— *500 × 7*

3500 − 1500 = 2000 more adults than children

Quick Test

1. Write these ratios as simply as possible:
   a) 5 : 35   **b)** 66 : 44   **c)** 5 cm : 1 m   **d)** 2 kg : 400 g

2. $\frac{1}{3}$ of the students in a class are girls.
   a) Write the number of girls to the number of boys as a ratio.
   b) There are 18 boys. How many girls are there?

3. Divide £36 in the ratio 4 : 5

4. Work out the largest part if 180 kg is divided in the ratio 2 : 3 : 5

Proportion

Direct Proportion

Two values are in **direct proportion** if the ratio between them remains fixed as the values change.

> **Example**
>
> If 2 bags of flour cost £2.36, how much do 3 cost?
>
> **Solution**
>
> 1 bag costs $\frac{2.36}{2}$ = £1.18
>
> So 3 bags cost 1.18 × 3 = £3.54

Speed, Distance and Time

To measure **speed** you need to know the **distance** travelled and the **time** taken.

$$\text{Speed} = \frac{\text{distance}}{\text{time}}$$

The **units** for speed are usually one of:

- miles per hour (mph)
- kilometres per hour (km/h)
- metres per second (m/s).

At constant speed, distance is **directly proportional** to time.

> **Example**
>
> A car travels 150 metres in 10 seconds. How far will it travel in 30 seconds at the same speed?
>
> **Solution**
>
> The car will travel
> 15 metres in 1 second.   ← Speed = 15 m/s
>
> It will travel 15 × 30
> = 450 metres in 30 seconds   ← Distance = speed × time

Density

To measure the **density** of an object you need to know the **mass** and the **volume**.

$$\text{Density} = \frac{\text{mass}}{\text{volume}}$$

The units for density are usually one of:

- grams per centimetre cubed (g/cm³)
- kilograms per metre cubed (kg/m³)

At a constant density, mass is **directly proportional** to volume.

> **Example**
>
> An object has mass 120 grams and volume 30 cm³. Work out the mass of a similar object that has a volume 8 times as big.
>
> **Solution A**
>
> As the volume is 8 times as big, the mass will be 8 times more. So mass is 120 × 8 = 960 grams
>
> **Solution B**
>
> Density is $\frac{120}{30}$ = 4 g/cm³   ← Density = $\frac{\text{mass}}{\text{volume}}$
>
> So for the similar object the volume is:
> 30 × 8 = 240 cm³
>
> So the mass of the similar object is:
> 240 × 4 = 960 grams   ← Mass = volume × density

Direct proportion • Speed • Unit • Density

Direct Proportion Graphs

If two quantities y and x are **directly proportional**, we write $y \propto x$ or $y = kx$ where k is called the **constant of proportionality**. The graph will be a straight line through the origin.

This is the graph $y = 2x$ so every y-value is twice the corresponding x-value.

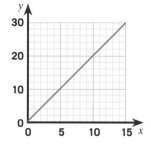

y can also be directly proportional to x^2 $(y \propto x^2)$, x^3 $(y \propto x^3)$, $\sqrt{x}$ $(y \propto \sqrt{x})$, $\sqrt[3]{x}$ $(y \propto \sqrt[3]{x})$, and so on.

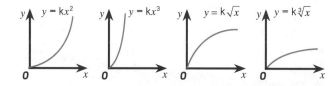

Example

y is directly proportional to the square of x.
When $y = 18$, $x = 3$

Work out the value of y when $x = 5$

Solution

We write $y \propto x^2$ or $y = kx^2$

$y = 18$, $x = 3$, so $18 = k \times 3^2$, giving k = 2

So $y = 2x^2$

When $x = 5$, $y = 2 \times 5^2 = 50$

Indirect (Inverse) Proportion Graphs

Two values are **indirectly** (or **inversely**) **proportional** if as one value increases, the other decreases in the same ratio, e.g. as one doubles, the other halves.

If two quantities y and x are indirectly proportional, we write $y \propto \frac{1}{x}$ or $y = \frac{k}{x}$

The graph will be a **reciprocal** curve as shown.

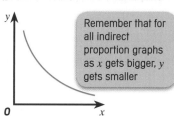

Remember that for all indirect proportion graphs as x gets bigger, y gets smaller

y can also be indirectly proportional to x^2 $\left(y \propto \frac{1}{x^2}\right)$, x^3 $\left(y \propto \frac{1}{x^3}\right)$, $\sqrt{x}$ $\left(y \propto \frac{1}{\sqrt{x}}\right)$, $\sqrt[3]{x}$ $\left(y \propto \frac{1}{\sqrt[3]{x}}\right)$, and so on.

Example

y is indirectly proportional to the cube root of x.
When $y = 2$, $x = 8$

Work out the value of y when $x = 27$

Solution

We write $y \propto \frac{1}{\sqrt[3]{x}}$ or $y = \frac{k}{\sqrt[3]{x}}$

$y = 2$, $x = 8$, so $2 = \frac{k}{\sqrt[3]{8}}$ giving k = 4

So $y = \frac{4}{\sqrt[3]{x}}$

When $x = 27$, $y = \frac{4}{\sqrt[3]{27}} = \frac{4}{3}$

Quick Test

1. y is directly proportional to x. When $y = 9$, $x = 3$
   Work out the value of y when $x = 4$

2. y is indirectly proportional to x^2. When $y = 50$, $x = 5$
   Work out the value of y when $x = 3$

Upper and Lower Bounds

Limits of Accuracy

Measurements are often rounded values. The actual value will be between the **lower bound** and the **upper bound**. The bounds are sometimes called the **limits of accuracy**.

You can show the limits of accuracy on a number line. For example, 8 cm to the nearest centimetre:

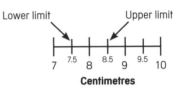

Discrete Data

Discrete data can only take **certain values** within a given range, e.g. number of people and amounts of money.

> ### Example
>
> At a football match, there are 3500 people to the nearest 100. What are the minimum and maximum number of people at the match?
>
> **Solution**
> 3450 is the lowest whole number that rounds to 3500 to the nearest 100.
>
> 3549 is the highest whole number that rounds to 3500 to the nearest 100.
>
> So minimum = 3450 and maximum = 3549

Continuous Data

Continuous data can take **any value** within a given range, e.g. length and time.

> ### Example
>
> A man is 1.8 metres tall to the nearest tenth of a metre.
>
> What is the shortest and tallest he could be?
>
> **Solution**
> 1.75 metres is the smallest possible value.
>
> 1.849 999 999 99... metres is the tallest he could be but 1.85 metres is the upper bound.
>
> So you write 1.75 m ≤ height of man < 1.85 m

Calculations using Upper and Lower Bounds

If two rounded values are added, subtracted, multiplied or divided, you can work out the **minimum** and **maximum** value possible by doing the calculations shown in the table.

	Minimum Value	Maximum Value
Addition $(x + y)$	$x_{min} + y_{min}$	$x_{max} + y_{max}$
Subtraction $(x - y)$	$x_{min} - y_{max}$	$x_{max} - y_{min}$
Multiplication $(x \times y)$	$x_{min} \times y_{min}$	$x_{max} \times y_{max}$
Division $(x \div y)$	$x_{min} \div y_{max}$	$x_{max} \div y_{min}$

Example

A rectangle has sides of 6 cm and 9 cm, to the nearest centimetre.

9 cm

6 cm

a) Work out the smallest possible perimeter.

Solution

Problem Solving

Remember that the perimeter of a rectangle = $2l + 2w$, where l = length and w = width. Use the lower bounds for the smallest possible perimeter.

The smallest possible perimeter uses the lower bounds, 5.5 cm and 8.5 cm.

Smallest possible perimeter is
5.5 + 8.5 + 5.5 + 8.5 = 28 cm

b) Work out the largest possible area.

Solution

Problem Solving

Remember that the area of a rectangle = lw, where l = length and w = width. Use the upper bounds for the largest possible area.

The largest possible area uses the upper bounds, 6.5 cm and 9.5 cm.

Largest possible area is $6.5 \times 9.5 = 61.75$ cm^2

Quick Test

1. Write down the upper and lower bounds for these values:
   a) 50 people given to the nearest 10
   b) 50 mph given to the nearest mile per hour
   c) 50 cm given to the nearest 5 cm
2. A woman runs 400 metres to the nearest metre. She takes 52 seconds to the nearest second. Work out her slowest and fastest possible average speed.

Recurring Decimals and Surds

Terminating and Recurring Decimals

A **terminating decimal** is a decimal that has a finite number of digits, e.g. $\frac{1}{2} = 0.5$ or $\frac{1}{4} = 0.25$

A **recurring decimal** has an infinite number of digits in a repeating pattern, e.g. $\frac{1}{3} = 0.333\ 333...$ or $\frac{2}{11} = 0.181\ 818...$

These recurring decimals are written as $0.\dot{3}$ and $0.\dot{1}\dot{8}$

Converting Fractions into Recurring Decimals

To convert a fraction into a decimal, divide the numerator by the denominator.

Example 1

Use a calculator to convert $\frac{2}{7}$ into a recurring decimal.

Solution

$2 \div 7 = 0.285\ 714\ 285\ 714...$

$\qquad = 0.\dot{2}85\ 71\dot{4}$

Example 2

Convert $\frac{2}{7}$ into a recurring decimal without using a calculator.

Solution

$$0.2\ 8\ 5\ 7\ 1\ 4\ 2...$$
$$7\,\overline{\smash{\big)}\,2.0^6 0^4 0^5 0^1 0^3 0^2 0...}$$

$\qquad = 0.\dot{2}85\ 71\dot{4}$

Converting Recurring Decimals into Fractions

You may be asked to convert recurring decimals into fractions.

Example

Convert $0.\dot{5}\dot{4}$ into a fraction.

Solution

> **Problem Solving**
>
> Write out the recurring decimal using digits. Identify the number of digits that recur. If N digits recur, multiply the recurring decimal by 10^N.

Let x be the fraction.

$$x = 0.545\ 454...$$

$$100x = 54.545\ 454...$$

> In this case two digits recur, so multiply by $10^2 = 100$

$$100x - x = 54.545\ 454... - 0.545\ 454...$$

$$99x = 54$$

> Subtract x to obtain a whole number

$$x = \frac{54}{99}$$

> Divide both sides by 99

Terminating decimal • Recurring decimal

Surds

A **rational number** is a number of the form $\frac{a}{b}$ where a and b are integers.

Surds are numbers left in **root form** that will **not simplify** to a rational number. $\sqrt{2}$ and $\sqrt[3]{5}$ are examples of surds. You will only need to work with square roots. A surd is an **exact answer**.

Example 1

Simplify:

a) $\sqrt{3} \times \sqrt{3}$

b) $\sqrt{75}$

> It will simplify because one factor of 75 is the square number 25

c) $\left(2+\sqrt{2}\right)^2$

> See *Expanding Brackets and Factorising*, pages 26–27

Solution

$\sqrt{3} \times \sqrt{3} = 3$

Solution

$\sqrt{75} = \sqrt{25 \times 3}$

$= \sqrt{25} \times \sqrt{3}$

$= 5\sqrt{3}$

Solution

$\left(2+\sqrt{2}\right)^2 = \left(2+\sqrt{2}\right)\left(2+\sqrt{2}\right)$

$= 4 + 2\sqrt{2} + 2\sqrt{2} + 2$

$= 6 + 4\sqrt{2}$

> This is the form $a + b\sqrt{2}$

Example 2

Work out the length x in the triangle. Give your answer as a surd.

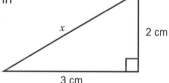

2 cm

3 cm

Solution

> **Problem Solving**
> The right-angled triangle is a clue that you will need to use Pythagoras' theorem (see page 64).

$x^2 = 3^2 + 2^2$

> $c^2 = a^2 + b^2$

$= 9 + 4 = 13$

$x = \sqrt{13}$ cm

> This is an exact value

Rationalising a Denominator

To **rationalise** a denominator is to make the denominator a rational number. To do this, multiply the numerator and denominator by the surd.

Example

Rationalise the denominator and simplify $\dfrac{10}{\sqrt{5}}$

Solution

$\dfrac{10}{\sqrt{5}} = \dfrac{10}{\sqrt{5}} \times \dfrac{\sqrt{5}}{\sqrt{5}}$

$= \dfrac{10\sqrt{5}}{5}$

> Cancel the 10 and the 5

$= 2\sqrt{5}$

Quick Test

1. Change these fractions into decimals:

   a) $\frac{2}{5}$ **b)** $\frac{4}{9}$ **c)** $\frac{3}{13}$

2. Change $0.\overset{..}{2}\overset{..}{1}$ into a fraction in its simplest form.

3. **a)** Simplify $\sqrt{18}$

   b) Write $\left(3+\sqrt{5}\right)^2$ in the form $a + b\sqrt{5}$

4. Rationalise the denominator and simplify $\dfrac{8}{\sqrt{2}}$

Basic Algebra

Algebra Facts

You need to know the meaning of these words:

- A **variable** is a letter that is used to represent any number, e.g. x or y.
- An **expression** is a combination of variables with numbers, e.g. $2x + 3y$ or $\frac{x}{2} + 1$
- An **equation** contains an equals sign and at least one variable, e.g. $2x + 5 = 16$ or $x + 3y = 7$
- A **formula** also contains an equals sign but is a rule connecting more than one variable, e.g. $A = \pi r^2$ or $s = \frac{d}{t}$
- An **identity** contains an identity sign and is true for all values, e.g. $x + x \equiv 2x$ or $(x + 5)^2 \equiv x^2 + 10x + 25$
- A **term** is one part of an expression, equation, formula or identity, e.g. $2x - 3y + 4$ has the three terms $2x$, $-3y$ and $+4$.
- An **integer** is a whole number.

Example

You are given that n is a positive integer.

Show clearly why $2n + 1$ is always odd.

Solution

> **Problem Solving**
>
> It's not enough to simply substitute values for n. This would only show it's true for those particular values.

An integer is a whole number.

$2 \times$ any positive whole number is always even. ← Multiples of 2 are even

Even + 1 = odd

So $2n + 1$ is always odd.

Collecting Like Terms

Like terms are terms with the same variable.
Here are some examples:

- $2x$ and $3x$
- $2xy$ and $3xy$
- x^2 and $4x^2$

To **simplify** an expression, you **collect like terms**.

Example

a) Simplify $3x + 4x$

Solution

$3x + 4x$ simplifies to $7x$

b) Simplify fully $x^2 + 4x - 7x + 3x^2$

Solution

$x^2 + 4x - 7x + 3x^2$
simplifies to $4x^2 - 3x$ ← $x^2 + 3x^2 = 4x^2$ and $+ 4x - 7x = -3x$

c) Simplify $xy + 3yx - 2xy$

Solution

$xy + 3yx - 2xy$
simplifies to $2xy$ ← Note that yx is the same as xy

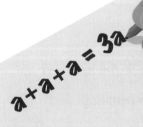

Key Words   Variable • Expression • Equation • Formula • Identity • Term • Integer • Like terms • Simplify

Substitution

Substitution is replacing variables (letters) with numbers.

> **Example**
>
> If $x = 2$, $y = -3$ and $z = 0$, work out the value of:
>
> **a)** $5x - 4y$
>
> **Solution**
>
> $5x - 4y = 5 \times 2 - 4 \times -3$ ← Substitute the values for x and y
>
> $= 10 + 12$ ← Show your working out
>
> $= 22$
>
> **b)** xyz
>
> **Solution**
>
> $xyz = 2 \times -3 \times 0$ ← Substitute the values for x, y and z
>
> $= 0$
>
> **c)** $y^2 - x$
>
> **Solution**
>
> $y^2 - x = (-3)^2 - 2$ ← Use brackets as the minus sign is also squared
>
> $= 9 - 2$ ← Show your working out
>
> $= 7$

Changing the Subject of a Formula

To **change the subject** of a formula:

1. collect all subject terms to one side of the formula
2. collect everything else to the other side
3. factorise (see page 26) if possible
4. rearrange to leave the subject on its own.

> **Example 1**
>
> Make x the subject of $y = 3x + 2$
>
> **Solution**
>
> $y - 2 = 3x$ ← Collect the subject term ($3x$) on one side and everything else on the other by subtracting 2 from both sides
>
> $\dfrac{y - 2}{3} = x$ ← Divide by 3 to leave the subject (x) on its own

> **Example 2**
>
> Make P the subject of $A = P + \dfrac{PRT}{100}$
>
> **Solution**
>
> $100A = 100P + PRT$ ← It's easier here to multiply by 100 first to remove the fractions
>
> $100A = P(100 + RT)$ ← Factorise as the subject P is a common factor
>
> $\dfrac{100A}{100 + RT} = P$ ← Rearrange to leave the subject (P) on its own

Quick Test

1. Simplify each of the following:
   a) $8x - 3x$
   b) $2x + 3y - 6x + 4y$
   c) $4x^2 + 5xy - 6x^2 + 4xy$
   d) $5x + 4y + 2x - 4y + z - 2z$
2. You are given that $x = 4$, $y = -\frac{1}{2}$ and $z = -1$. Work out the value of:
   a) $2x + 6y$
   b) $3x + y - 4z$
   c) $xy - yz$
3. Make x the subject of:
   a) $y + 2x = y(6 + x)$
   b) $y = \dfrac{x + 2}{x - 3}$

Expanding Brackets and Factorising

Expanding Brackets

To **expand** or **multiply out** brackets, every term in the bracket is multiplied by the term outside the bracket.

To multiply out two brackets, each term in the second bracket is multiplied by each term in the first bracket. The result is called a **quadratic expression**.

Example 1

a) Multiply out $5(x + 4)$

Solution

$5(x + 4) = 5x + 20$

b) Expand and simplify $9(x - 3) - 2(3x - 4)$

Solution

$9(x - 3) - 2(3x - 4)$

$= 9x - 27 - 6x + 8$ ← Multiply out each bracket separately

$= 3x - 19$ ← Collect like terms

Example 2

Expand and simplify:

a) $(x + 5)(x - 3)$

Solution

$(x + 5)(x - 3) = x(x - 3) + 5(x - 3)$

$= x^2 - 3x + 5x - 15$ ← Multiply out each bracket separately

$= x^2 + 2x - 15$ ← Collect like terms

b) $(2x - 7)(3x - 1)$

Solution

$(2x - 7)(3x - 1) = 2x(3x - 1) - 7(3x - 1)$

$= 6x^2 - 2x - 21x + 7$ ← Multiply out each bracket separately

$= 6x^2 - 23x + 7$

Example 3

Prove that the square of any odd number is always 1 more than a multiple of 8.

Solution

Problem Solving
Set up an expression using the information given.

If n is an integer, $2n + 1$ must be odd.

When you double a whole number and add 1, you will always get an odd number

$(2n + 1)^2$ ← You have set up an expression for the square of any odd number

$= 4n^2 + 2n + 2n + 1$ ← Expand the brackets

$= 4n^2 + 4n + 1$ ← Collect the terms

$= 4n(n + 1) + 1$ ← Factorise the first two terms

$n(n + 1)$ is even so it's a multiple of 2. ← Odd × even or even × odd

So $4n(n + 1)$ is a multiple of 8.

Factorisation

Factorisation is the reverse process of multiplying out brackets. To factorise you have to look for **common factors** in every term.

Example

Factorise:

a) $3x + 6$ **Solution** $3x + 6 = 3(x + 2)$

b) $4x^2 + 3x$ **Solution** $4x^2 + 3x = x(4x + 3)$

c) $8xy - 6x^2$ **Solution** $8xy - 6x^2 = 2x(4y - 3x)$

$2x$ is the highest common factor of $8xy$ and $-6x^2$

Factorising Quadratic Expressions

Expressions of the Form $x^2 + bx + c$

To factorise a quadratic expression of this form:

1. write out the brackets as $(x \quad)(x \quad)$
2. use this table to decide the signs in the brackets:

	c is Positive	c is Negative
b is Positive	$(x +)(x +)$	$(x +)(x -)$
b is Negative	$(x -)(x -)$	$(x +)(x -)$

3. test numbers which multiply together to give c and add together to give b.

> **Example**
>
> Factorise $x^2 - x - 12$
>
> **Solution**
>
> $(x +)(x -)$ ← b is negative and c is negative
>
> $= (x + 3)(x - 4)$ ← $3 \times -4 = -12$ and $3 + -4 = -1$
>
> Check $(x + 3)(x - 4) = x(x - 4) + 3(x - 4)$
>
> $= x^2 - 4x + 3x - 12$
>
> $= x^2 - x - 12$

Expressions of the Form $ax^2 + bx + c$

To factorise a quadratic expression of this form:

1. write out the brackets as $(px \quad)(qx \quad)$ where $pq = a$
2. use this table to decide the signs in the brackets:

	c is Positive	c is Negative
b is Positive	$(px +)(qx +)$	$(px +)(qx -)$
b is Negative	$(px -)(qx -)$	$(px +)(qx -)$

3. test numbers which multiply together to give c
4. multiply out all the possible combinations until you find the correct pairing.

> **Example**
>
> Factorise $2x^2 + 7x + 3$
>
> **Solution**
>
> $(x +)(2x +)$ ← $pq = 2$, b is positive and c is positive
>
> $= (x + 3)(2x + 1)$
>
> Check $(x + 3)(2x + 1) = x(2x + 1) + 3(2x + 1)$
>
> $= 2x^2 + x + 6x + 3$
>
> $= 2x^2 + 7x + 3$

Difference of Two Squares

A quadratic expression of the form $a^2 - b^2$ is called a **difference of two squares**, e.g. $x^2 - 25$ or $4x^2 - 49y^2$.

$a^2 - b^2$ factorises as $(a - b)(a + b)$.

> **Example 1**
>
> Factorise $4x^2 - 49y^2$
>
> Notice that $4x^2$ is $(2x)^2$ and $49y^2$ is $(7y)^2$ so this is a difference of two squares
>
> **Solution**
>
> $4x^2 - 49y^2 = (2x)^2 - (7y)^2$
>
> $= (2x - 7y)(2x + 7y)$

> **Example 2**
>
> Simplify $\frac{9x^2 - 4}{3x^2 + x - 2}$
>
> Factorising the numerator and denominator
>
> Cancelling the common factor $(3x - 2)$
>
> **Solution**
>
> $\frac{9x^2 - 4}{3x^2 + x - 2}$
>
> $= \frac{(3x - 2)(3x + 2)}{(3x - 2)(x + 1)}$
>
> $= \frac{(3x + 2)}{(x + 1)}$

Quick Test

1. Multiply out $5(2x + 3)$
2. Expand and simplify $(x + 3)(x - 5)$
3. Factorise:
   a) $8x^2 - 12x$ b) $x^2 - 3x + 2$
   c) $3x^2 - 11x - 20$ d) $x^2 - 16y^2$

Linear Equations

Equations

An **equation** has an unknown value to be worked out. This is called **solving** the equation.

You should already know how to solve **one-step linear equations**.

Example

Solve:

a) $x + 4 = 7$ **Solution** $x = 3$ Subtract 4 from both sides

b) $x - 5 = 11$ **Solution** $x = 16$

c) $2x = 8$ **Solution** $x = 4$

d) $\dfrac{x}{10} = 3$ **Solution** $x = 30$ Multiply both sides by 10

Using the Balance Method to Solve Equations

The sides of an equation should **balance**.
So whatever you do to one side of the equation, you must also do to the other side.

Example 1

Solve $2x + 3 = 11$

Solution

$$2x + 3 = 11$$
$$ - 3 - 3$$

Subtract 3 from both sides of the equation to leave just the x-term on the left-hand side. Note that +3 and −3 give a zero, shown by the circle

$$2x = 8$$
$$\frac{2x}{2} = \frac{8}{2}$$

Divide both sides by 2 to leave just x on the left-hand side

$$x = 4$$

Example 2

Solve $8x - 5 = 4x + 3$

Solution

$$8x - 5 = 4x + 3$$
$$ + 5 + 5$$

Add 5 to both sides of the equation to leave just the x-term on the left-hand side. Note that −5 and +5 give a zero, shown by the circle

$$8x = 4x + 8$$
$$- 4x - 4x$$

Subtract $4x$ from both sides of the equation to leave just the number 8 on the right-hand side. Note that $4x$ and $-4x$ give a zero, shown by the circle

$$4x = 8$$
$$\frac{4x}{4} = \frac{8}{4}$$

Divide both sides by 4 to leave just x on the left-hand side

$$x = 2$$

Example 3

Solve $6(2x - 1) = 5(2x + 4)$

Solution

$$12x - 6 = 10x + 20$$

← Multiply out the brackets on both sides

$$12x \boxed{- 6} = 10x + 20$$
$$ + 6 + 6$$

← Add 6 to both sides of the equation to leave just the x-term on the left-hand side. Note that −6 and +6 give a zero, shown by the circle

$$12x = \boxed{10x} + 26$$
$$- 10x \boxed{- 10x}$$

← Subtract $10x$ from both sides of the equation to leave just the number 26 on the right-hand side. Note that $10x$ and $-10x$ give a zero, shown by the circle

$$2x = 26$$

$$\frac{2x}{2} = \frac{26}{2}$$

← Divide both sides by 2 to leave just x on the left-hand side

$$x = 13$$

Example 4

The sum of x, $4x$ and $x + 1$ is 43. Work out the value of x.

Solution

Problem Solving

Always set up an equation to work out the answer. If you use trial and improvement, you may not find the answer. Once you have set up the equation, solve it as normal.

$$x + 4x + x + 1 = 43$$

$$6x \boxed{+ 1} = 43$$
$$\boxed{- 1} = - 1$$

← Subtract 1 from both sides of the equation to leave just the x-term on the left-hand side

$$6x = 42$$

$$\frac{6x}{6} = \frac{42}{6}$$

← Divide both sides by 6 to leave just x on the left-hand side

$$x = 7$$

Quick Test

Solve these equations.

1. **a)** $5x - 7 = 8$
    b) $7x - 1 = 13$
    c) $6x + 5 = 2x$
2. **a)** $3x + 5 = x - 9$
    b) $8x - 1 = 3x + 9$
    c) $\frac{1}{2}x - 2 = 7 - x$
3. **a)** $6(2x + 1) = 3(x + 11)$
    b) $3(2x - 5) = 2(x - 2)$
    c) $8(x - 1) = 5(x + 1)$

Quadratic Equations

Solving Quadratic Equations by Factorising

To solve a **quadratic equation** by **factorising**:
1. write the equation into the form $ax^2 + bx + c = 0$
2. factorise $ax^2 + bx + c$
3. equate each bracket to zero
4. solve the linear equations.

Example 1

Solve $x^2 - 5x + 6 = 0$

Solution

$x^2 - 5x + 6 = 0$

$(x - 2)(x - 3) = 0$

So $x - 2 = 0$ or $x - 3 = 0$

$x = 2$ or $x = 3$

Example 2

Solve $2x^2 + 7x - 4 = 0$

Solution

$2x^2 + 7x - 4 = 0$

$(2x - 1)(x + 4) = 0$

So $2x - 1 = 0$ or $x + 4 = 0$

$2x = 1$ or $x = -4$

$x = \frac{1}{2}$ or $x = -4$

Example 3

The solutions of a quadratic equation are $x = 2$ and $x = -4$

Work out the equation.

Solution

Problem Solving

To obtain the quadratic equation, work backwards from the solutions.

$x = 2$ and $x = -4$

So $x - 2 = 0$ or $x + 4 = 0$ ← Set up the linear equations

So $(x - 2)(x + 4) = 0$ ← Combine the equations to form a quadratic

$x^2 + 2x - 8 = 0$ ← Expand the brackets

Solving Quadratic Equations by Completing the Square

To **complete the square** of a quadratic equation of the form $x^2 + bx + c = 0$:
1. write the equation into the form $x^2 + bx + c = 0$
2. rewrite $x^2 + bx$ as $(x + \frac{b}{2})^2 - (\frac{b}{2})^2$
3. remember to add c back on
4. solve the equation.

Example 1

Solve $x^2 - 8x - 6 = 0$ by completing the square.

Solution

$x^2 - 8x - 6 = 0$

$(x - 4)^2 - (-4)^2 - 6 = 0$

$(x - 4)^2 - 16 - 6 = 0$

$(x - 4)^2 = 22$ ← Add 16 and 6 to both sides

$x - 4 = \pm\sqrt{22}$ ← Take the square root of both sides

$x = 4 \pm\sqrt{22}$ ← Answer in surd form

$x = 8.69$ or $x = -0.69$ ← Answers given to 2 decimal places

Key Words   **Quadratic equation • Complete the square**

Example 2

Here is an identity:

$x^2 + 6x - 5 \equiv (x + a)^2 + b$

a) Work out the values of a and b.

Solution

> **Problem Solving**
>
> To work out a compare the x-terms and to work out b compare the constants.

$(x + a)^2 + b$ expanded gives $x^2 + 2ax + a^2 + b$

So $x^2 + 6x - 5 \equiv x^2 + 2ax + a^2 + b$

Comparing the x-terms:

$6 = 2a$, so $a = 3$ ← This is called equating coefficients of x

Comparing the constants:

$-5 = a^2 + b$

So $-5 = 9 + b$

$b = -14$

b) Solve $x^2 + 6x - 5 = 0$

Solution

$x^2 + 6x - 5 = 0$

So $(x + 3)^2 - 9 - 5 = 0$

$(x + 3)^2 - 14 = 0$

$(x + 3)^2 = 14$ ← Add 14 to both sides

$x + 3 = \pm\sqrt{14}$ ← Take the square root of both sides

$x = -3 \pm\sqrt{14}$ ← Answer in surd form

$x = 0.74$ or $x = -6.74$ ← Answers given to 2 decimal places

Solving Quadratic Equations by using the Quadratic Formula

Quadratic equations of the form $ax^2 + bx + c = 0$ can be solved using the **quadratic formula**:

$$x = \frac{-b \pm \sqrt{b^2 - 4ac}}{2a}$$

Quick Test

1. Solve by factorising:
   a) $x^2 - 11x + 18 = 0$
   b) $3x^2 - 14x - 5 = 0$
2. Solve by completing the square.
   Give your answer in surd form.
   a) $x^2 - 6x + 4 = 0$
   b) $x^2 + 3x - 11 = 0$
3. Solve by using the quadratic formula:
   a) $2x^2 + x - 8 = 0$
   b) $3x^2 - 7x + 1 = 0$

Example

Solve $5x^2 + 2x - 4 = 0$

Give your answers to 2 decimal places. ← This is a clue that the quadratic will not factorise

Solution

$a = 5$, $b = 2$, $c = -4$

> Substitute for a, b and c in the formula

So $x = \dfrac{-(2) \pm \sqrt{(2)^2 - 4 \times (5) \times (-4)}}{2 \times (5)}$

$x = \dfrac{-2 \pm \sqrt{4 + 80}}{10}$

$x = \dfrac{-2 \pm \sqrt{84}}{10}$

$x = \dfrac{-2 + \sqrt{84}}{10}$ or $x = \dfrac{-2 - \sqrt{84}}{10}$

$x = 0.72$ or $x = -1.12$

Trial and Improvement & Sequences

Trial and Improvement

You can use **trial and improvement** to solve equations. It involves trying values and improving them to get as close as possible to the solution.

Example 1

Use trial and improvement to find the solution to $x^3 = 30$. Give your answer to 1 decimal place.

Solution

x	x^3	Comment
3	27	Too small
4	64	Too big
3.2	32.768	Too big
3.1	29.791	Too small
3.15	31.255 875	Too big

Solution between $x = 3$ and $x = 4$

Solution between $x = 3.1$ and $x = 3.2$

The solution is between $x = 3.1$ and $x = 3.15$
So to 1 decimal place, the solution is $x = 3.1$

Example 2

Show that the equation $x^3 - 12x = 50$ has a solution between 4 and 5.

Solution

> **Problem Solving**
> Write the equation with all terms on one side, then complete a table to present your answer clearly and logically.

$x^3 - 12x - 50 = 0$

x	$x^3 - 12x - 50$	Comment
4	$4^3 - (12 \times 4) - 50 = -34$	Too small
5	$5^3 - (12 \times 5) - 50 = 15$	Too big

So the solution is between 4 and 5.

Number Patterns and Sequences

You should be familiar with these number sequences:

- **Odd** numbers:
  1   3   5   7   9   …
- **Even** numbers:
  2   4   6   8   10   …
- **Square** numbers:
  1   4   9   16   25   …
- **Cube** numbers:
  1   8   27   64   125   …

You also need to know the following:

- A **sequence** is a set of numbers with a rule to find each number.
- A **term-to-term rule** is a rule that links one term to the next term, e.g. the term-to-term rule for odd numbers is 'add 2'.
- A **position-to-term rule** is a rule that links the position of the term to the term, e.g. the position-to-term rule for odd numbers is 'double the position number and subtract 1':

Position	1	2	3	4	5
Term	1	3	5	7	9

So the 5th term is $2 \times 5 - 1 = 9$

The nth Term of a Sequence

The nth term of a sequence is a formula for the position-to-term rule, e.g. the formula for the nth term for odd numbers would be $2n - 1$.

N.B. A common mistake is to give the term-to-term rule as the nth term.

Key Words   Trial and improvement • Sequence • Term-to-term rule • Position-to-term rule

Trial and Improvement & Sequences

Example 1

Work out the nth term of this sequence:

7   10   13   16   19   …

Solution

The term-to-term rule is 'add 3':

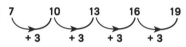

So the sequence is linked to the 3 times table.

So the nth term will be of the form $3n + c$.

When $n = 1$: $3 \times 1 + c = 7$, so $c = 4$

So the nth term is $3n + 4$.

Example 2

Work out the nth term of this sequence:

11   9   7   5   …

Solution

The term-to-term rule is 'subtract 2':

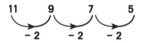

So the sequence is linked to the 2 times table.

So the nth term will be of the form $-2n + c$.

When $n = 1$: $-2 \times 1 + c = 11$, so $c = 13$

So the nth term is $-2n + 13$ or $13 - 2n$.

Quick Test

1. Use trial and improvement to find a solution to 1 decimal place.
   a) $x^3 = 20$ **b)** $x^3 - 10x + 6 = 0$
2. For each sequence:
   i) write down the next two terms
   ii) work out the nth term
   iii) work out the 20th term.
   a) 5   8   11   14   17   …
   b) 10   14   18   22   26   …

Example 3

A café has tables to seat 4 people. When put together 2 tables can seat 6 people, and so on.

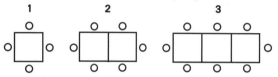

How many people can sit at n tables in this way?

Solution

Position	1	2	3
Term	4	6	8

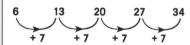

The term-to-term rule is 'add 2'.

So the nth term will be of the form $2n + c$.

When $n = 1$: $2 \times 1 + c = 4$, so $c = 2$

So the nth term is $2n + 2$.

The number of people at n tables is $2n + 2$.

Example 4

Jack says that 87 is in this sequence:

6   13   20   27   34   …

Is he correct? You must show your working.

Solution

> **Problem Solving**
>
> To test if a number is part of a sequence, work out the nth term and test if an integer value for n gives that number.

The term-to-term rule is 'add 7':

6   13   20   27   34
  + 7   + 7   + 7   + 7

So the nth term will be of the form $7n + c$.

When $n = 1$: $7 \times 1 + c = 6$, so $c = -1$

So the nth term is $7n - 1$.

Solving $7n - 1 = 87$ gives $n = 12.57$

So 87 is between the 12th and 13th terms.

> The 12th term is $7 \times 12 - 1 = 83$ and the 13th term is $7 \times 13 - 1 = 90$

Jack isn't correct.

Straight Line Graphs

Linear Graphs

A **linear graph** is a straight line graph, e.g. $y = x$, $y = 2x + 3$, $x + y = 5$, etc.

To draw the graph:

1. choose three values for x (pick any three easy values in the range of the graph – the highest and lowest are often sensible points to use)
2. work out the corresponding y-values
3. plot the points on a grid
4. draw a straight, ruled line through the points.

Example 1

Draw the graph of $y = 2x + 3$ for values of x from -2 to 2.

Solution

Choosing $x = -2$, $x = 0$ and $x = 2$ ← Choose three values for x

When $x = -2$
$y = 2 \times -2 + 3 = -1$ ← Work out each corresponding y-value

When $x = 0$
$y = 2 \times 0 + 3 = 3$

When $x = 2$
$y = 2 \times 2 + 3 = 7$

x	-2	0	2
y	-1	3	7

This gives the points to plot on the grid: $(-2, -1)$, $(0, 3)$ and $(2, 7)$

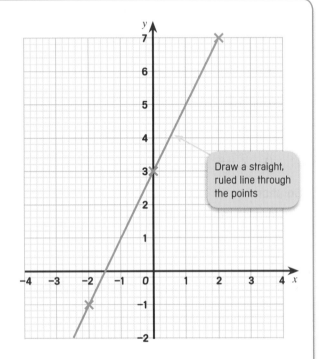

Draw a straight, ruled line through the points

Example 2

Draw the graph of $x + y = 5$ for values of x from 0 to 5.

Solution

Choosing $x = 0$, $x = 2$ and $x = 5$ ← Choose three values for x

When $x = 0$, $y = 5$
When $x = 2$, $y = 3$ ← Work out each corresponding y-value
When $x = 5$, $y = 0$

x	0	2	5
y	5	3	0

This gives the points to plot on the grid: $(0, 5)$, $(2, 3)$ and $(5, 0)$

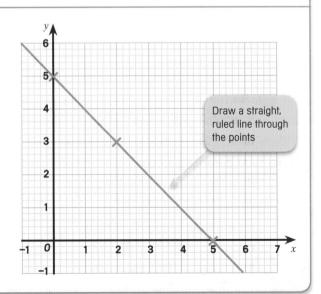

Draw a straight, ruled line through the points

Gradient

Gradient is a measure of the amount a line slopes. To work out the gradient of a straight line:

1 choose two points on the line and join them

2 draw a right-angled triangle, using the line already drawn as the hypotenuse

3 use the formula:

> **Gradient** = $\dfrac{\text{distance up the triangle}}{\text{distance across the triangle}}$
>
> or
>
> **Gradient** = $\dfrac{\text{difference of } y\text{-coordinates}}{\text{difference of } x\text{-coordinates}}$

Remember the following about lines and their gradients:

- A line sloping up from left to right has a **positive** gradient and a line sloping down from left to right has a **negative** gradient.
- Lines that are **parallel** have the same gradient.
- Lines that are **perpendicular** are at right angles to each other.

Example

Work out the gradient of these straight lines.

a)
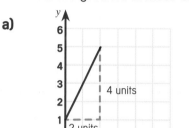

Solution

Gradient = $\dfrac{\text{distance up the triangle}}{\text{distance across the triangle}} = \dfrac{4}{2} = 2$

b)
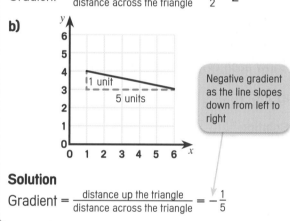

Negative gradient as the line slopes down from left to right

Solution

Gradient = $\dfrac{\text{distance up the triangle}}{\text{distance across the triangle}} = -\dfrac{1}{5}$

$y = mx + c$

Equations of straight lines are often written in the form **$y = mx + c$**, where:

- m is the gradient
- c is the y-intercept.

The y-intercept is the point where the line crosses the y-axis.

Quick Test

1 Work out the gradient and the coordinates of the y-intercept of $2y = 3x + 6$

2 Which of these lines are parallel?

$y = 3x + 1$	$x = 3y + 1$
$6x - 2y = 9$	$3x + y = 4$

Example

Write down the gradient and the coordinates of the y-intercept in each case.

a) $y = 3x + 2$

Solution

Gradient = 3, y-intercept is (0, 2)

b) $x + 2y = 5$

Solution

Rearranging the equation $x + 2y = 5$ gives:

Problem Solving

Write the equation in the form $y = mx + c$

$y = -0.5x + 2.5$ ← Divide both sides by 2

Gradient = -0.5, y-intercept is (0, 2.5)

Linear Inequalities

Inequality Symbols

Inequalities use the symbols:

- $<$ to mean 'less than'
- $>$ to mean 'greater than'
- $\leq$ to mean 'less than or equal to'
- $\geq$ to mean 'greater than or equal to'.

Inequalities on a Number Line

The solution to an inequality can be shown on a **number line** using open circles (O) and closed circles (●):

means $x <$
means $x >$
means $x \leq$
means $x \geq$

Example

Show each of these inequalities on a number line:

a) $x < 1$

Solution

b) $x > 4$

Solution

c) $x \leq 1$

Solution

d) $x \geq 4$

Solution

e) $-2 \leq x < 5$

Solution

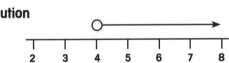

Solving Linear Inequalities

When solving a **linear inequality**:

- use the same techniques as when solving an equation
- always collect terms so that the x-term has a positive coefficient
- never replace the inequality symbol with an equals sign.

Key Words   Inequality • Number line • Linear inequality

Example

a) Solve $3x - 3 \geqslant x + 7$

Solution

$3x - 3 \geqslant x + 7$

$2x - 3 \geqslant 7$ ← Subtract x from both sides

$2x \geqslant 10$ ← Add 3 to both sides

$x \geqslant 5$ ← Divide both sides by 2

b) Solve $-2x > 6$

Solution

$-2x > 6$

$-6 - 2x > 0$ ← Subtract 6 from both sides

$-6 > 2x$ ← Add $2x$ to both sides

$-3 > x$ or $x < -3$ ← If -3 is greater than x, then x is less than -3

c) Work out the integers that satisfy $6 < 3x \leqslant 12$

Solution

$6 < 3x \leqslant 12$

$2 < x \leqslant 4$ ← Divide through by 3

3 and 4 satisfy the inequality.

↑ Integers are the whole numbers that satisfy the inequality

Representing Inequalities on a Graph

A linear inequality can be shown by a region on a graph. The region will lie on one side of the straight line graph for the corresponding equation, e.g.:

- $x < 3$ is the region to the left of the line $x = 3$
- $y \geqslant 4$ is the region above and including the line $y = 4$

You should also know the following:

- For $x <$ or $x >$ a dotted line is used to show that the points on the line are **not** included.
- For $x \leqslant$ or $x \geqslant$ a solid line is used to show that the points on the line are included.

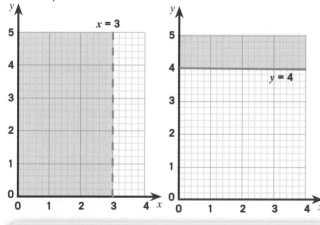

Example

Show graphically the region, R, that satisfies $x \leqslant 2$, $y \geqslant x$ and $y < 2x$

Solution

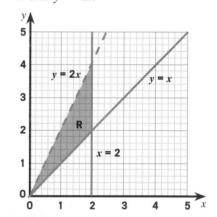

Check your answer by choosing a point in the region and testing that it satisfies all the inequalities

For example, (1.5, 2.5) is in the region marked and $x = 1.5$, $y = 2.5$ obeys all three inequalities.

$x \leqslant 2$, $y \geqslant x$ and $y < 2x$ ← $1.5 < 2$, $2.5 > 1.5$ and $2.5 < 3$

Quick Test

1. Show each inequality on a number line: **a)** $x \leqslant 3$ **b)** $0 < x \leqslant 4$
2. Solve these inequalities: **a)** $2x - 8 > 0$ **b)** $2(x + 3) \geqslant 9$
3. Show graphically the region, R, that satisfies $x > 1$, $x \leqslant 2$, $y \geqslant x + 1$ and $y < 4$

Simultaneous Equations

To solve a pair of **simultaneous equations** is to find the pair (or pairs) of solutions that satisfy both equations.

Elimination and Substitution Methods

To solve by **eliminating** variables, follow these steps:
1. Match the **coefficients** of one of the variables.
2. Eliminate this variable by adding or subtracting the equations.
3. Solve the linear equation in the remaining variable.
4. Substitute this value back into one of the original equations.
5. Solve this linear equation in the remaining variable.
6. Check that your solutions satisfy both the original equations.

To solve by **substitution**, follow these steps:
1. Rearrange one equation into the form $y = \ldots$ or $x = \ldots$
2. Substitute for y or x in the other equation.
3. Solve the equation in the remaining variable.
4. Substitute this value back into the rearranged equation.
5. Solve this linear equation in the remaining variable.
6. Check that your solutions satisfy both the original equations.

Example

Solve the simultaneous equations $3x + 2y = 7$ and $x - y = -1$

Solution

$3x + 2y = 7$

$x - y = -1$ ← To match the coefficients of y, multiply this equation by 2

$3x + 2y = 7$
$2x - 2y = -2$ ← To eliminate y, add the equations, i.e. **different** signs: **add**

$5x = 5$ ← Divide both sides by 5

$x = 1$

$3 + 2y = 7$ ← Substitute back into the first equation

$2y = 4$ ← Subtract 3 from both sides

$y = 2$

Check:

$3x + 2y = 7$ $3 + 4 = 7$ ✓

$x - y = -1$ $1 - 2 = -1$ ✓

Example

Solve the simultaneous equations $5x + 3y = 12$ and $3x + 2y = 7$

Solution

$5x = 12 - 3y$ ← Subtract $3y$ from both sides of $5x + 3y = 12$

$x = \dfrac{12 - 3y}{5}$ ← Divide by 5

$3\left(\dfrac{12 - 3y}{5}\right) + 2y = 7$ ← Substitute for x in the equation $3x + 2y = 7$

$3(12 - 3y) + 10y = 35$ ← Multiply both sides by 5

$36 - 9y + 10y = 35$ ← Expand the bracket

$y = -1$ ← Collect terms and subtract 36 from both sides

So $x = \dfrac{12 - 3(-1)}{5}$ ← Substitute $y = -1$ into the equation $x = \dfrac{12 - 3y}{5}$

$x = 3$

Check:

$5x + 3y = 12$ $15 - 3 = 12$ ✓

$3x + 2y = 7$ $9 - 2 = 7$ ✓

Other Simultaneous Equations

Use the substitution method to solve simultaneous equations with one linear and one of the form $ax^2 + bx + c = 0$, where a, b and c are integers.

Example

Solve the simultaneous equations $y = 7 - 2x$ and $y = 2x^2 + 3$

Solution

$7 - 2x = 2x^2 + 3$ ← Substitute $y = 7 - 2x$ into the equation $y = 2x^2 + 3$

$0 = 2x^2 + 2x - 4$ ← Collect terms to one side

$0 = x^2 + x - 2$ ← Divide both sides by 2

$0 = (x + 2)(x - 1)$ ← Factorise

$x = -2$ or $x = 1$

When $x = -2$, $y = 11$ and when $x = 1$, $y = 5$ ← Substitute both the x-values into $y = 7 - 2x$ to find corresponding y-values

Solving Simultaneous Equations Graphically

To solve simultaneous equations graphically:

1. draw the graphs of the two equations
2. the solutions are the point(s) of intersection.

Example 1

Solve $x + y = 5$ and $2x + y = 7$

Solution

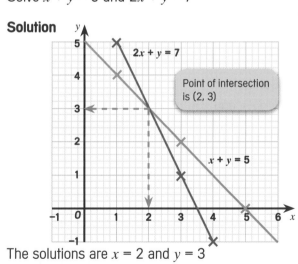

Point of intersection is (2, 3)

The solutions are $x = 2$ and $y = 3$

Check: $x + y = 5$ $2 + 3 = 5$ ✓
        $2x + y = 7$ $4 + 3 = 7$ ✓

Example 2

Solve graphically the simultaneous equations $y - x = 4$ and $y = 2x^2$

Solution

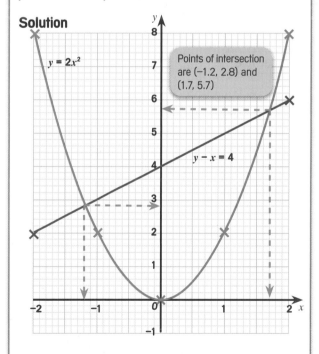

Points of intersection are (−1.2, 2.8) and (1.7, 5.7)

The solutions are $x = -1.2$, $y = 2.8$ and $x = 1.7$, $y = 5.7$

Check: Approximate answers as read from the graph

$y - x = 4$ $2.8 - -1.2 = 4$ and $5.7 - 1.7 = 4$ ✓
$y = 2x^2$ $2(-1.2)^2 = 2.88$ and $2(1.7)^2 = 5.78$ ✓

Quick Test

1. Solve $4x + 3y = 23$ and $3x - 2y = 13$
2. Solve $y = x + 1$ and $y = x^2 - 3x + 4$

Harder Equations and Graphs

Harder Algebraic Equations

To achieve the highest grades, you need to be able
to solve harder algebraic equations.

Example

Solve $\dfrac{3}{2x-1} - \dfrac{4}{3x-1} = 1$

Solution

$$\frac{3(3x-1)}{(2x-1)(3x-1)} - \frac{4(2x-1)}{(2x-1)(3x-1)} = \frac{(2x-1)(3x-1)}{(2x-1)(3x-1)}$$

Obtaining a common denominator

$$3(3x-1) - 4(2x-1) = (2x-1)(3x-1)$$

Equating the numerator

$$9x - 3 - 8x + 4 = 6x^2 - 2x - 3x + 1$$

Expanding brackets

$$0 = 6x^2 - 6x$$

Collecting like terms

$$0 = 6x(x-1)$$

Factorising

So $x = 0$ or $x = 1$

Quadratic Graphs

A **quadratic graph** is a curved graph

 or $\cap$.

To draw a quadratic graph:
1. complete a table of values
2. plot the points and draw a smooth curve.

Example

a) Draw the graph of $y = 2x^2 - x - 3$ for values
of x from -1 to 2.

Solution

x	-1	0	1	2
$2x^2$	2	0	2	8
$-x$	1	0	-1	-2
-3	-3	-3	-3	-3
y	0	-3	-2	3

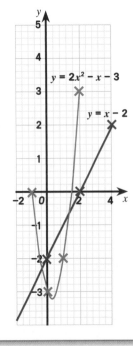

b) Use the graph to solve $2x^2 - x - 3 = 0$

Solution

$x = -1$ and $x = 1.5$

Read off at the points where $y = 0$

c) Use the graph to solve $2x^2 - 2x - 1 = 0$

Solution

The graph drawn is $y = 2x^2 - x - 3$

The equation to solve is $0 = 2x^2 - 2x - 1$

$$\begin{array}{r} y = 2x^2 - x - 3 \\ - \quad 0 = 2x^2 - 2x - 1 \\ \hline y = x - 2 \end{array}$$

Subtract the equations

Draw the line $y = x - 2$ on the graph

This gives solutions $x = -0.4$ and $x = 1.4$

Read off at the points of intersection

Graphs of Cubic, Reciprocal and Exponential Functions

You need to know the following:

- A **cubic** function is of the form
  $y = ax^3 + bx^2 + cx + d$,
  e.g. $y = x^3$ or $y = 2x^3 + 4x + 3$

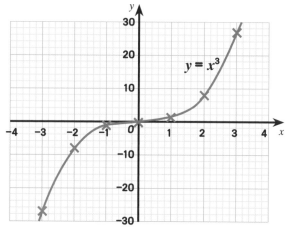

- A **reciprocal** function is of the form $y = \frac{k}{x}$ with
  $x \neq 0$, e.g. $y = \frac{1}{x}$ or $y = \frac{3}{x}$

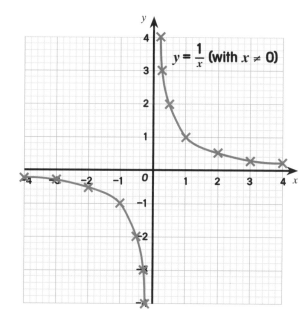

- An **exponential** function is of the form $y = k^x$,
  e.g. $y = 2^x$ or $y = 3^x$

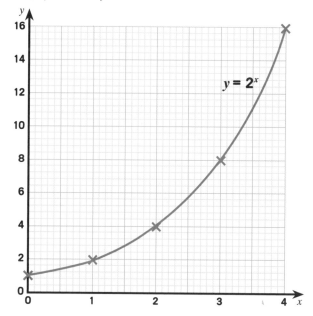

You'll need to plot these types of graphs from a table of values.

Quick Test

1. Draw the graph of $y = x^2 - 2x - 2$ for values of x from -2 to 4.
2. Sketch the graphs of:
   a) $y = x^3$
   b) $y = \frac{1}{x}$
   c) $y = 2^x$

Trigonometrical Graphs and Transformations

Graphs of Trigonometrical Functions

Here are the graphs of $y = \sin x$ and $y = \cos x$ for values of x from $-360°$ to $+360°$.

The graph of $y = \sin x$:
- is **cyclic** (the shape repeats indefinitely in both directions)
- has line symmetry about $x = 90°$
- has rotational symmetry about $(180°, 0)$.

The graph of $y = \cos x$:
- is **cyclic**
- has line symmetry about $x = 0°$
- has rotational symmetry about $(90°, 0)$.

You'll need to plot graphs of these types from a table of values.

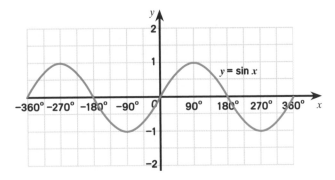

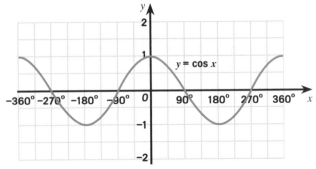

Example

Given that $\cos 60 = 0.5$, use the graph $y = \cos x$ to work out:

a) $\cos 300°$

Solution

> **Problem Solving**
> Use the symmetrical properties of the graph. In this case use line symmetry with mirror line $x = 180°$

$y = \cos x$ has line symmetry about $x = 180°$ so $\cos 300° = 0.5$

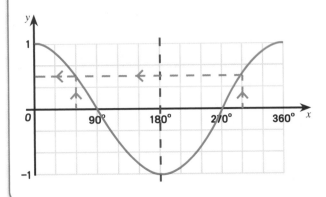

b) $\cos 120°$

Solution

> **Problem Solving**
> Use the symmetrical properties of the graph. In this case use rotational symmetry about $(90°, 0)$.

$y = \cos x$ has rotational symmetry about $(90°, 0)$ so $\cos 120° = -0.5$

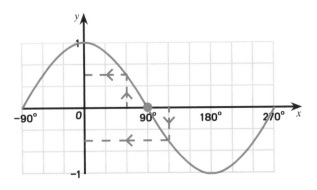

Key Words Cyclic

Trigonometrical Graphs and Transformations

Transformations of Graphs

The notation $y = f(x)$ is used to represent any graph where $f(x)$ is any **function** of x.

From a graph of $y = f(x)$, you'll need to draw the graphs of:

- $y = f(x) + a \longrightarrow$ A translation of $y = f(x)$ by the **vector** $\begin{pmatrix} 0 \\ a \end{pmatrix}$

- $y = f(x + a) \longrightarrow$ A translation of $y = f(x)$ by the vector $\begin{pmatrix} -a \\ 0 \end{pmatrix}$

- $y = af(x) \longrightarrow$ A stretch of $y = f(x)$, scale factor a in the y-direction

- $y = f(ax) \longrightarrow$ A stretch of $y = f(x)$, scale factor $\frac{1}{a}$ in the x-direction

- $y = -f(x) \longrightarrow$ A reflection of $y = f(x)$ in the x-axis

- $y = f(-x) \longrightarrow$ A reflection of $y = f(x)$ in the y-axis.

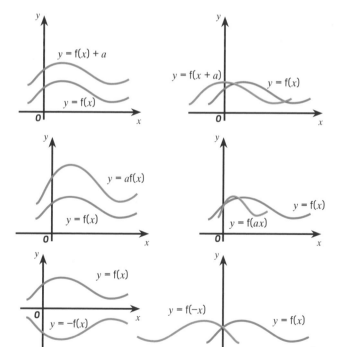

Example

The diagram shows the graph of $y = \sin x$ for values of x from $0°$ to $360°$.

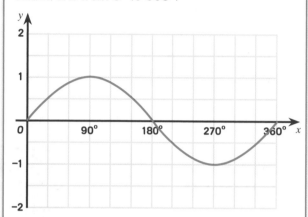

Draw the graphs of:

a) $y = 1 + \sin x$

Solution

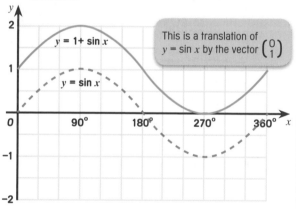

This is a translation of $y = \sin x$ by the vector $\begin{pmatrix} 0 \\ 1 \end{pmatrix}$

b) $y = 2 \sin x$

Solution

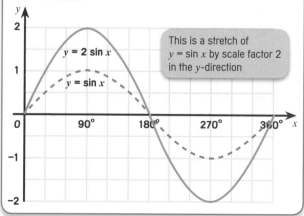

This is a stretch of $y = \sin x$ by scale factor 2 in the y-direction

Exam Practice Questions

You may wish to answer these questions on a separate piece of paper so that you can show full working out, which you will be expected to do in the exam.

Questions labelled with an asterisk (*) are ones where the quality of your written communication (QWC) will be assessed.

1.   **a)** Solve $8(1 + 4x) - 4(x + 3) = 0$

_____ *(3 marks)*

  b) Solve $\frac{y}{2} - 5 = 11$

_____ *(2 marks)*

*2. Matt wants a new fridge. Three shops have these adverts for the fridge he wants.

Matt wants to pay as little as possible.

From which shop should he buy the fridge?

Show clearly how you get your answer.

_____

_____ *(6 marks)*

3.   The nth term of a sequence is $n^2 + 5$.

  a) Find the sixth term of the sequence.

_____ *(2 marks)*

  b) Is the number 125 a term in the sequence?

    Give reasons for your answer.

_____

_____ *(2 marks)*

*4. Abby and Jude share £84 in the ratio 7 : 5

Abby says that she gets £15 more than Jude.

Is she correct? You **must** show your working out clearly.

(4 marks)

5. Mr Smith bought a new car for £16 500 in January 2008.

He sold it for £6900 in January 2011.

a) Work out the average annual depreciation of the car.

(2 marks)

b) Estimate the value of the car in January 2012.

(2 marks)

6. **a)** Express 42 as a product of prime factors.

(2 marks)

b) Express 42^2 as a product of prime factors.

(1 mark)

7. Jack has £5 more than Kylie.

Kylie has half as much as Liam.

Liam has £x.

Jack and Kylie give their money to Liam.

Liam now has £20.

a) Show that $x + \frac{x}{2} + \frac{x}{2} + 5 = 20$

(2 marks)

*b) How much did Liam have to start with?

(3 marks)

8. **a)** Work out $2\frac{1}{4} + 1\frac{2}{3}$

(2 marks)

b) Work out $3\frac{1}{3} \times 1\frac{1}{2}$

(3 marks)

9. Clare spent £168 on her monthly shop. This was 20% more than last month.

How much was her monthly shop last month?

.... (3 marks)

10. **a)** Factorise fully $8xy - 12y^2$

.... (2 marks)

b) Factorise $2x^2 - 5x - 3$

.... (2 marks)

11. Harry earned £15 000 last year. He does not pay tax on the first £5040.

Kim earned £14 400 last year. She does not pay tax on the first £8100.

They both pay tax on 20% of the rest of their earnings.

*a) Who pays the most tax and by how much?

.... (4 marks)

*b) Who takes home the most pay and by how much?

.... (2 marks)

12. **a)** The Sun measures 1.4 million kilometres across. Write this as a number in standard form.

.... (1 mark)

b) Light travels at 3×10^8 metres per second. Write this as an ordinary number.

.... (1 mark)

13. Write down the equation of the line that is parallel to the line $y = 3x - 2$ and passes through the point (0, 4).

.... (1 mark)

*14. In an electrical circuit, the current (I) is indirectly proportional to the resistance (R).

When I = 10 amps, R = 24 ohms

Explain what happens to the current when the resistance doubles.

Show working to support your answer.

.... (4 marks)

15. **a)** Write $(3 + \sqrt{5})^2$ in the form $a + b\sqrt{5}$

_____ *(2 marks)*

b) Rationalise the denominator and simplify $\dfrac{10}{\sqrt{2}}$

_____ *(2 marks)*

16. The diagram shows the graph of $y = x^2$

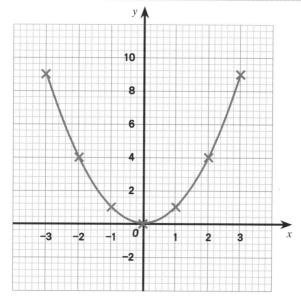

a) On the same grid sketch the graph of $y = x^2 - 2$ *(1 mark)*

b) Write down the coordinates of the vertex of the curve with equation $y = (x + 1)^2$

_____ *(1 mark)*

17. The y-coordinate of a point P is 2 less than its x-coordinate.

a) On the grid, draw the graph of the set of points P.

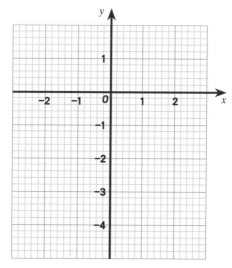

(2 marks)

b) Write down the equation of your graph.

_____ *(1 mark)*

Angles and Parallel Lines

Angle Facts

Acute angles are less than 90°.

Obtuse angles are between 90° and 180°.

Reflex angles are between 180° and 360°.

Angles **on a straight line** add up to **180°**.

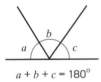

$$a + b + c = 180°$$

Angles **at a point** add up to **360°**.

$$a + b + c + d = 360°$$

Vertically opposite angles are **equal**.

$$a = b$$
$$c = d$$

Parallel Lines

Alternate angles are equal.

Corresponding angles are equal.

 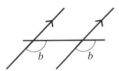

Allied angles add up to 180°.

$$c + d = 180°$$

Example

Work out the value of x.

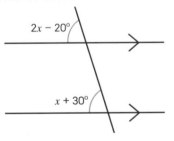

Solution

Problem Solving

To answer this type of question you need to set up an equation and then solve it.

$$2x - 20 = x + 30$$
$$+ 20 \qquad + 20 \quad \leftarrow \text{Add 20 to both sides}$$

$$2x = x + 50$$
$$- x \qquad - x \quad \leftarrow \text{Subtract } x \text{ from both sides}$$

$$x = 50°$$

Key Words   Acute angle • Obtuse angle • Reflex angle • Alternate angles

Example 1

Work out the value of x.

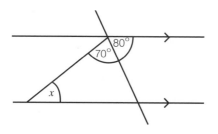

Problem Solving

Because there are parallel lines, look out for any alternate or corresponding angles.

Solution A

Filling in the missing angle on the straight line gives 30°.

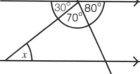

x and 30° are alternate angles, so $x = 30°$

Solution B

The other angle in the triangle and 80° are alternate angles.

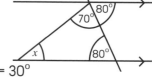

Angles in a triangle add up to 180°, so x is $180° - 70° - 80° = 30°$

Example 2

Show that AC is parallel to DG.

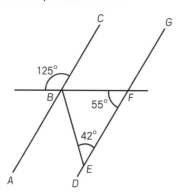

Solution

Problem Solving

Mark any missing angles you know on the diagram.

Angle CBF is $180° - 125° = 55°$ ← Angles on a straight line

Angle CBF = angle BFE, so they are alternate angles on parallel lines AC and DG.

N.B. You don't use the angle of 42° to answer the question.

Quick Test

1. In each part, work out the value of x.
   Give reasons for your answers.

a)

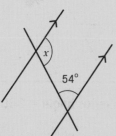

b)

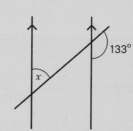

c)

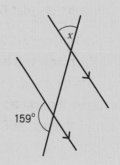

Angles of Polygons

Polygon Facts

You should know the following:

- A **polygon** is a shape made from straight sides, e.g. a **triangle**, a **quadrilateral**, a **pentagon**, and so on.
- **Interior angles** are the angles inside a polygon.
- **Exterior angles** are formed by extending one side of a polygon as shown in the diagram below.
- A **vertex** is a point where two sides meet, i.e. a corner.

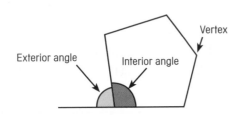

At any vertex:

> **Interior angle + exterior angle = 180°**

Polygons can be divided into triangles. This hexagon has been divided into four triangles. So the sum of its interior angles is:

4 × 180° = 720°

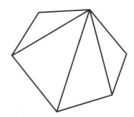

> **Sum of interior angles of any polygon** $= \left(\begin{array}{c}\text{number of}\\\text{sides} - 2\end{array}\right) \times 180°$

Name	Triangle	Quadrilateral	Pentagon	Hexagon	Octagon	Decagon
Number of Sides	3	4	5	6	8	10
Sum of Interior Angles	180°	360°	540°	720°	1080°	1440°

Regular Polygons

A **regular polygon** has:

- all sides of equal length
- all interior angles of equal size
- all exterior angles of equal size
- line symmetry, e.g. a regular hexagon has six sides and six lines of symmetry
- rotational symmetry, e.g. a regular hexagon has rotational symmetry of order 6.

Imagine you are walking around the edge of a regular hexagon. Each time you turn at a vertex, you turn through the exterior angle. To return to the start, you have turned through all six exterior angles and you have turned through 360°.

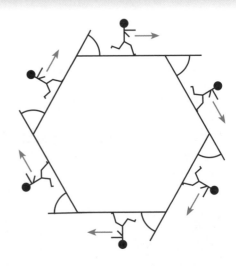

So:

> **Number of sides × exterior angle = 360°**
>
> or
>
> **Exterior angle** $= \dfrac{360°}{\text{number of sides}}$

Example 1

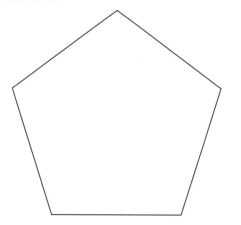

a) Work out the size of each exterior angle of a regular pentagon.

Solution

A regular pentagon has five sides.

Exterior angle of a regular pentagon is:

$\frac{360°}{5} = 72°$

b) Work out the size of each interior angle of a regular pentagon.

Solution

Interior angle + exterior angle = 180°

Interior angle of a regular pentagon is:
180° − 72° = 108°

Quick Test

1 Work out the size of the interior and exterior angles of these regular shapes:

a) Octagon   **b)** Decagon

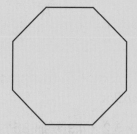   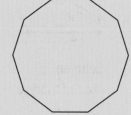

Example 2

The diagram shows a regular hexagon *ABCDEF*. Work out the size of the angle marked *x*.

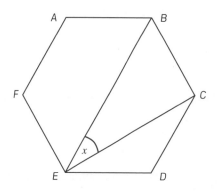

Solution

> **Problem Solving**
>
> Break this type of question into several steps. First find the exterior angle and use this to find the interior angle. Then use properties of isosceles triangles.

Exterior angle of a regular hexagon is:

$\frac{360°}{6} = 60°$

Interior angle + exterior angle = 180°

Interior angle of a regular hexagon is:
180° − 60° = 120°

So angle *FED* = 120°

EB bisects angle *FED*

So angle *FEB* is $\frac{120°}{2} = 60°$

Triangle *EDC* is isosceles

So angle *DEC* is $\frac{(180° - 120°)}{2} = 30°$

So *x* is 120° − 60° − 30° = 30°

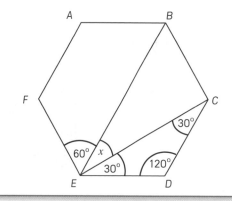

Areas of Triangles and Quadrilaterals

Area Calculations

Area of a Triangle

If you know the length of the base and the **perpendicular** height, you can use the following formula to work out the area of a triangle:

Area of triangle $= \frac{1}{2} \times$ base $\times$ perpendicular height

$$A = \frac{1}{2}bh$$

or

Area of triangle $= \dfrac{\text{base} \times \text{perpendicular height}}{2}$

$$A = \frac{bh}{2}$$

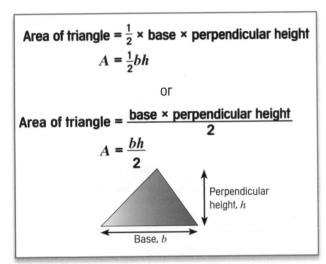

Perpendicular height, h

Base, b

If you know the length of two sides and the angle between them, you can use this formula to work out the area:

Area of triangle $= \frac{1}{2}ab\sin C$

N.B. This formula is given on the formulae page of the examination paper.

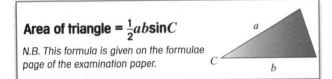

Area of a Trapezium

Area of **trapezium** $= \frac{1}{2}(a + b)h$

N.B. This formula is given on the formulae page of the examination paper.

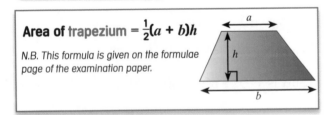

Area of a Parallelogram

Area of **parallelogram** $= $ base $\times$ perpendicular height

$$A = bh$$

Example 1

Work out the area of these shapes:

a)

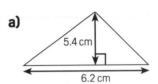

5.4 cm

6.2 cm

Solution

Area of triangle $= \dfrac{\text{base} \times \text{perpendicular height}}{2}$

$\qquad = \dfrac{6.2 \times 5.4}{2}$

$\qquad = 16.74 \text{ cm}^2$

b)

3.5 cm

4 cm

7.5 cm

Solution

Area of trapezium $= \frac{1}{2}(a + b)h$

$\qquad = \frac{1}{2}(3.5 + 7.5)4$

$\qquad = 22 \text{ cm}^2$

c)

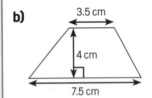

6 cm

7 cm

8 cm

Solution

Area of parallelogram $=$ base $\times$ perpendicular height

$\qquad = 8 \times 6$

$\qquad = 48 \text{ cm}^2$

Don't mix up the perpendicular height with the sloping height

d)

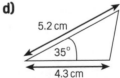

5.2 cm

35°

4.3 cm

Solution

Area of triangle $= \frac{1}{2}ab\sin C$

$\qquad = \frac{1}{2} \times 5.2 \times 4.3 \times \sin 35°$

$\qquad = 6.4 \text{ cm}^2$ (to 1 d.p.)

Example 2

The total area of this shape is 37.31 cm².

Work out the perpendicular height of the triangle.

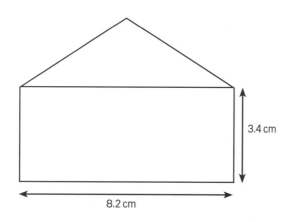

8.2 cm

3.4 cm

Solution

Problem Solving

You know the formula for the area of a triangle is $A = \frac{1}{2}bh$. You have all the information you need to find A and b, so then you can rearrange the formula to calculate h.

Area of rectangle is $8.2 \times 3.4 = 27.88$ cm²

Area of triangle is $37.31 - 27.88 = 9.43$ cm²

$$\frac{\text{base} \times \text{perpendicular height}}{2} = 9.43$$

$$\frac{8.2 \times \text{perpendicular height}}{2} = 9.43$$

$$\text{Perpendicular height of triangle} = \frac{9.43 \times 2}{8.2}$$

$$= 2.3 \text{ cm}$$

Example 3

The length of a rectangle is 3 cm more than its width. The area of the rectangle is 108 cm².

Work out the length of the rectangle.

Solution

Problem Solving

Set up an equation using the information given and solve it. Draw a sketch if it helps.

Let the width of the rectangle be x cm.

So the length is $(x + 3)$ cm.

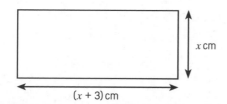

x cm

$(x + 3)$ cm

Length × width = area of rectangle

So $x(x + 3) = 108$

$x^2 + 3x - 108 = 0$ ← Now you can see that there is a quadratic equation to solve

$(x + 12)(x - 9) = 0$

So $x + 12 = 0$ or $x - 9 = 0$

So $x = 9$ ← $x = -12$ is impossible as you can't have a negative width

Width of rectangle = 9 cm
and length of rectangle = 12 cm

Quick Test

① Work out the areas of these shapes. Give your answers to 2 decimal places.

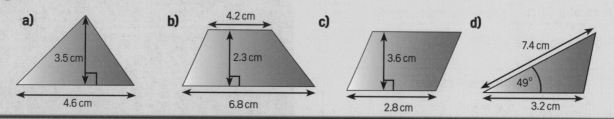

a) 3.5 cm   4.6 cm

b) 4.2 cm   2.3 cm   6.8 cm

c) 3.6 cm   2.8 cm

d) 7.4 cm   49°   3.2 cm

Circumference and Area of Circles

Circle Facts

You need to know the following:

- The **circumference** of a circle is the distance around the edge of the circle.
- The **radius** of a circle is a straight line from the centre to the circumference.
- The **diameter** is a straight line through the centre joining opposite points on the circumference.
- A **chord** is a straight line joining any two points on the circumference.
- A **tangent** is a straight line that touches the circumference of a circle.
- An **arc** is a part of the circumference of a circle.
- A **sector** is the area enclosed by two radii and an arc.
- A **segment** is the area between a chord and its arc.

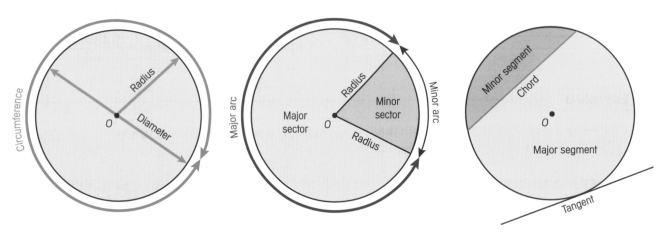

Calculations with Circles

Circumference of a Circle

Circumference is the word used to mean the **perimeter** of a circle.

The circumference of a circle is given by:

> **Circumference** = π × **diameter**
>
> $$C = \pi d$$
>
> or
>
> **Circumference** = 2 × π × **radius**
>
> $$C = 2\pi r$$

Area of a Circle

The area of a circle is given by:

> **Area** = π × **radius**²
>
> $$A = \pi r^2$$

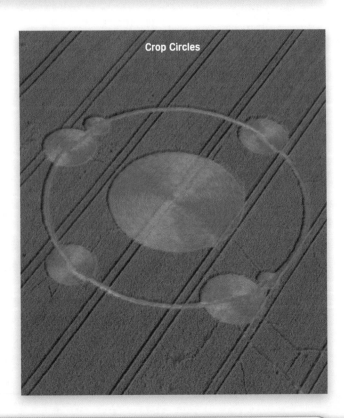

Crop Circles

Key Words   Circumference • Radius • Diameter • Chord • Tangent • Arc • Sector • Segment • Perimeter

Circumference and Area of Circles

Example 1

a) Work out the circumference of this circle. Give your answer to 2 decimal places.

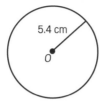

5.4 cm

O

Solution

$C = 2\pi r$

$= 2 \times \pi \times 5.4$

> Remember to write down more than 2 decimal places before rounding

$= 33.929...$

> You could get the same answer by working out the diameter (2 × 5.4 = 10.8 cm), then using the formula $C = \pi d$

$= 33.93$ cm

b) Work out the area of the circle. Give your answer to 2 decimal places.

Solution

$A = \pi r^2 = \pi \times 5.4 \times 5.4$

$= 91.608...$

$= 91.61$ cm^2

Example 2

a) Work out the circumference of this circle. Give your answer in terms of π.

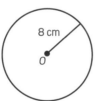

8 cm

O

Solution

$C = 2\pi r = 2 \times \pi \times 8$

$= 16\pi$ cm

> Again, you could get the same answer by working out the diameter (2 × 8 = 16 cm), then using the formula $C = \pi d$. If you're asked to give an answer in terms of π, then leave the π symbol in your answer

b) Work out the area of the circle. Give your answer in terms of π.

Solution

$A = \pi r^2 = \pi \times 8 \times 8$

$= 64\pi$ cm^2

Example 3

Work out the perimeter of this semicircle. Give your answer to 2 decimal places.

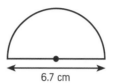

6.7 cm

Solution

Problem Solving
When asked to work out the perimeter, remember to calculate all the lengths of the shape you are given (in this case the length of the circular arc of the semicircle plus the diameter).

Length of circular arc $= \frac{1}{2}(\pi \times 6.7) = 10.524...$

Perimeter is length of circular arc + diameter =
10.524... + 6.7

$= 17.22$ cm

Quick Test

① Work out **i)** the circumference and **ii)** the area of these circles.
Give your answers to 1 decimal place.
a) A circle of radius 4.7 cm
b) A circle of diameter 6.1 cm
c) A circle of radius 2.4 cm

② Work out **i)** the circumference and **ii)** the area of these circles.
Give your answers in terms of π.
a) A circle of diameter 10 cm
b) A circle of radius 6 cm

Arc Length and Area of a Sector

Circumference and Area of a Circle

You need to remember the following:

> **Circumference of a circle = π × diameter**
>
> $$C = \pi d$$
>
> or
>
> **Circumference of a circle = 2 × π × radius**
>
> $$C = 2\pi r$$

> **Area of a circle = π × radius²**
>
> $$A = \pi r^2$$

Arc Length and Area of a Sector

Arc Length of a Circle

An **arc** is part of the circumference of a circle.
The length of an arc is given by:

> **Arc length = $\dfrac{\text{angle at centre}}{360°}$ × circumference of circle**

An arc that is:
- smaller than a semicircular arc is called a **minor arc**
- bigger than a semicircular arc is called a **major arc**.

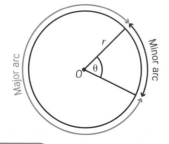

Area of a Sector of a Circle

A **sector** is the area enclosed by two radii and an arc. The area of a sector is given by:

> **Area of sector = $\dfrac{\text{angle at centre}}{360°}$ × area of circle**

A sector that is:
- smaller than a semicircle is called a **minor sector**
- bigger than a semicircle is called a **major sector**.

Example 1

Work out the arc length and area of the sector shown. Give your answers to 1 decimal place.

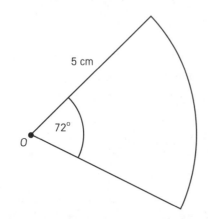

Solution

$$\text{Arc length} = \frac{\text{angle at centre}}{360°} \times \text{circumference of circle}$$

$$= \frac{72°}{360°} \times 2 \times \pi \times 5$$

$$= 6.3 \text{ cm}$$

$$\text{Area of sector} = \frac{\text{angle at centre}}{360°} \times \text{area of circle}$$

$$= \frac{72°}{360°} \times \pi \times 5^2$$

$$= 15.7 \text{ cm}^2$$

Example 2

The diagram shows a keyhole shape.

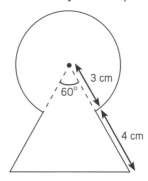

a) Work out the perimeter of the shape. Give your answer to 1 decimal place.

Solution

Problem Solving

Break down the diagram into parts you can recognise (in this case an arc and three straight lines). Remember that the perimeter is just the length of the outside edge, i.e.

Triangle is equilateral so length of base = 7 cm

Angle at centre for major arc is $360° - 60° = 300°$

$$\text{Length of major arc} = \frac{\text{angle at centre}}{360°} \times \text{circumference of circle}$$

$$= \frac{300°}{360°} \times 2 \times \pi \times 3$$

$$= 15.70... \text{ cm}$$

So the perimeter of the shape is:

$15.70... + 4 + 4 + 7 = 30.7$ cm

b) Work out the area of the keyhole shape.

Give your answer to 1 decimal place.

Solution

Problem Solving

Break down the diagram into shapes you can recognise.

$$\text{Area of circle} = \pi \times 3^2$$

$$= 28.27... \text{ cm}^2$$

$$\text{Area of triangle} = \frac{1}{2} \times 7 \times 7 \times \sin 60°$$

$$= 21.21... \text{ cm}^2$$

$$\text{Area of minor sector} = \frac{\text{angle at centre}}{360°} \times \text{area of circle}$$

$$= \frac{60°}{360°} \times \pi \times 3^2$$

$$= 4.71... \text{ cm}^2$$

Total area of the keyhole shape is given by:

$$\text{Area of circle} + \text{area of triangle} - \text{area of minor sector}$$

$= 28.27... + 21.21... - 4.71...$

$= 44.77...$

$= 44.8 \text{ cm}^2$

Quick Test

1. Work out **i)** the arc length and **ii)** the area of these sectors. Give your answers to 1 decimal place.

   a) 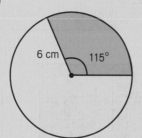 **b)** 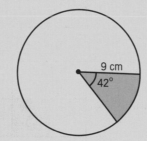 **c)**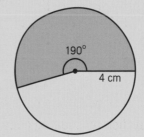

Plan and Elevation

A **plan view** of a 3-D shape is what you
see when you look at it from above.

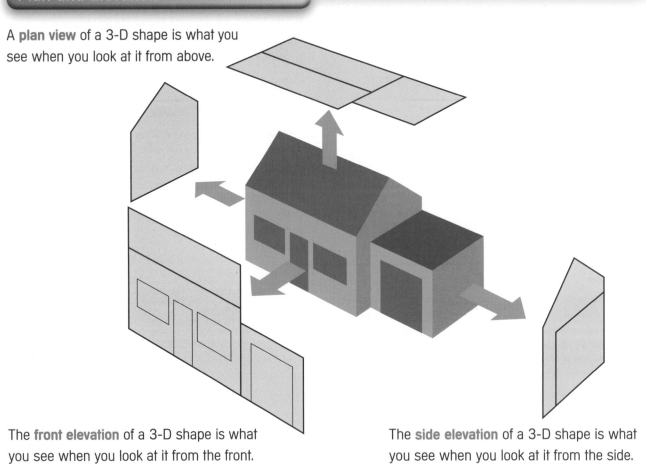

The **front elevation** of a 3-D shape is what
you see when you look at it from the front.

The **side elevation** of a 3-D shape is what
you see when you look at it from the side.

Example 1

Here is a 3-D shape made of centimetre cubes
drawn on isometric paper:

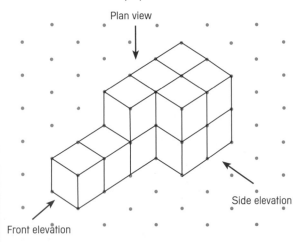

Plan view

Side elevation

Front elevation

Draw **a)** the plan view, **b)** the front elevation and
c) the side elevation on squared paper.

Solution

a)

b)

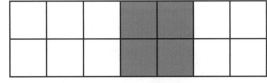

c)

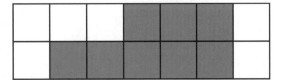

Example 2

Here are the three views of a 3-D shape:

Plan view

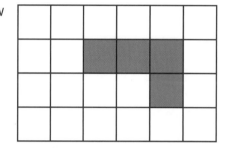

Front elevation

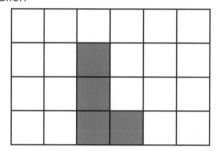

Side elevation

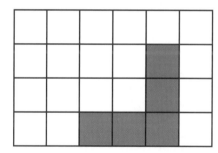

Draw the 3-D shape on isometric paper.

Solution

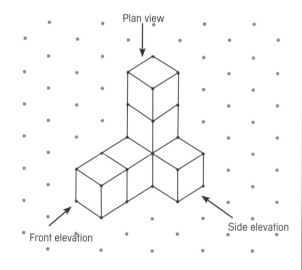

Quick Test

1. For each shape draw on squared paper:
   i) the plan view
   ii) the front elevation
   iii) the side elevation.

a)

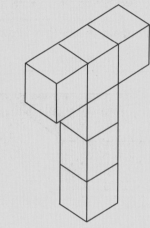

b)

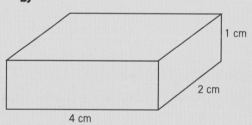

c)

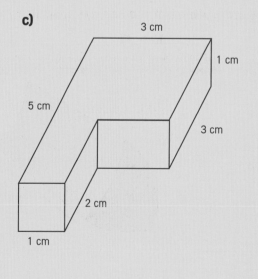

Volumes of Prisms

Volume Facts

You should know the following:

- **Volume** is the amount of space a 3-D shape fills.
- Common units for volume are cm³ and m³.

Volume of a Cuboid

Volume of a cuboid = length × width × height

$$V = lwh$$

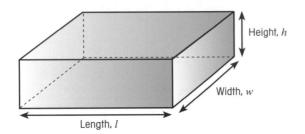

Height, h

Width, w

Length, l

Example

Work out the volume of this cuboid.

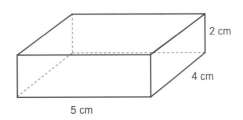

2 cm

4 cm

5 cm

Solution

Volume of cuboid = length × width × height

Volume = 5 × 4 × 2

= 40 cm³

Volume of a Prism

A **prism** is a 3-D shape that has **uniform cross-section**.

Volume of a prism = area of cross-section × length

$$V = Al$$

N.B. You're given this formula in the examination.

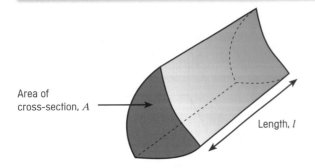

Area of cross-section, A

Length, l

Example

Work out the volume of this prism.

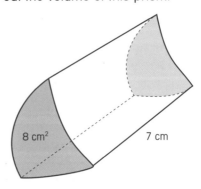

8 cm²

7 cm

Solution

Volume of prism = area of cross-section × length

Volume = 8 × 7

= 56 cm³

Volumes of Cylinders and Triangular Prisms

Cylinders and **triangular prisms** are special types of prism.

The cross-section of a cylinder is a circle, so:
- the area of the circle (πr^2) is the area of the cross-section
- the volume of a cylinder = area of circle × height ($V = \pi r^2 h$)

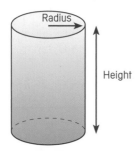

The cross-section of a triangular prism is a triangle, so:
- the area of the triangle ($\frac{1}{2}$ × base × height) is the area of the cross-section
- the volume of a triangular prism = area of triangle × length

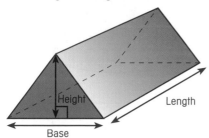

Quick Test

1. Work out the volume of these solids:
   a) A prism with cross-section 12 cm² and length 5 cm.
   b) A cylinder of height 4.2 cm and radius 6.1 cm.
   c) A triangular prism with base 4 cm, perpendicular height 3 cm and length 7 cm.

Example 1

Work out the volume of a cylinder of radius 4 cm and height 10 cm.

Solution

Volume of cylinder = $\pi \times 4^2 \times 10$ ← Area of circle × height

= 160π cm³ or 502.7 cm³

Example 2

Work out the volume of this triangular prism.

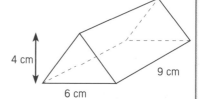

Solution

Area of triangle = $\frac{1}{2} \times 6 \times 4$ ← $\frac{1}{2}$ × base × height

= 12 cm²

Volume of prism = 12 × 9 ← Area of cross-section × length

= 108 cm³

Example 3

You are given that 1 litre = 1000 cm³

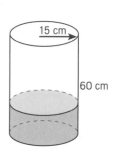

A cylindrical water tank is $\frac{1}{4}$ full. How many more litres of water are needed to fill the tank?

Solution

Problem Solving
Work out the volume of the whole shape, then work out the fraction you need. In this case you need $\frac{3}{4}$ of the total volume.

Volume of full tank = $\pi \times 15 \times 15 \times 60$

= 42 412 cm³

Volume of $\frac{3}{4}$ of tank is $\frac{42\ 412}{4} \times 3 = 31\ 809$ cm³

So approximately 31.8 litres are needed to fill the tank.

Key Words — Cylinder • Triangular prism

Volumes of Pyramids, Cones and Spheres

Volume of a Pyramid

$$\text{Volume of pyramid} = \frac{1}{3} \times \text{area of base} \times \text{vertical height}$$
$$V = \frac{1}{3}Ah$$

Example

Work out the volume of this pyramid.

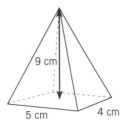

9 cm

5 cm   4 cm

Solution

$$\text{Volume of pyramid} = \frac{1}{3} \times \text{area of base} \times \text{vertical height}$$

$$\text{Volume} = \frac{1}{3} \times 5 \times 4 \times 9$$

$$= 60 \text{ cm}^3$$

Volume of a Cone

A **cone** is a pyramid with a circular base.

Volume of a pyramid $= \frac{1}{3} \times$ area of base $\times$ vertical height

So:

$$\text{Volume of cone} = \frac{1}{3} \times \pi r^2 \times h$$
$$V = \frac{1}{3}\pi r^2 h$$

N.B. You're given this formula in the examination.

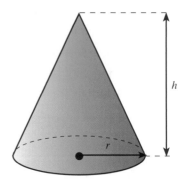

Example

Work out the volume of this cone.

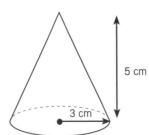

5 cm

3 cm

Solution

$$\text{Volume of cone} = \frac{1}{3}\pi r^2 h$$

$$\text{Volume} = \frac{1}{3} \times \pi \times 3 \times 3 \times 5$$

$$= 15\pi \text{ cm}^3 \text{ or } 47.1 \text{ cm}^3$$

Volume of a Sphere

$$\text{Volume of sphere} = \frac{4}{3}\pi r^3$$

N.B. You're given this formula in the examination.

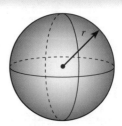

Volumes of Pyramids, Cones and Spheres

Example

Work out the volume of this sphere.

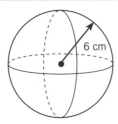

6 cm

Solution

Volume of sphere $= \frac{4}{3}\pi r^3$

Volume $= \frac{4}{3} \times \pi \times 6^3$

$= 288\pi$ cm^3 or 904.8 cm^3

Hemispheres and Frustums

A **hemisphere** is half a sphere.

Volume of hemisphere $= \frac{2}{3}\pi r^3$

A **frustum** is the remainder of a regular solid whose upper part has been cut off by a plane parallel to the base.

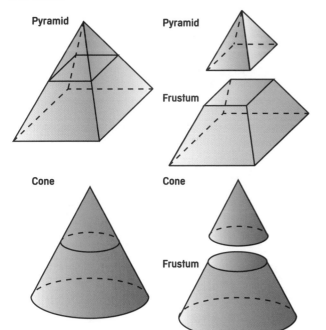

Pyramid

Pyramid

Frustum

Cone

Cone

Frustum

Example

A frustum is made from pyramid A by removing pyramid B. The base of pyramid A is a square of side 8 cm and the height is 12 cm. The base of pyramid B is a square of side 3 cm and the height is 4.5 cm. Work out the volume of the frustum.

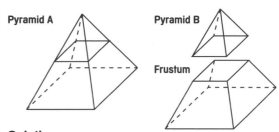

Pyramid A

Pyramid B

Frustum

Solution

> **Problem Solving**
>
> Work out the volume of each pyramid. Subtract the volume of the smaller pyramid from the volume of the larger one.

Volume of pyramid A $= \frac{1}{3} \times 8 \times 8 \times 12$

$= 256$ cm^3

Volume of pyramid B $= \frac{1}{3} \times 3 \times 3 \times 4.5$

$= 13.5$ cm^3

So volume of frustum is $256 - 13.5$

$= 242.5$ cm^3

Quick Test

1. Work out the volume of these solids. Give your answers to 1 decimal place.
   a) A hemisphere of radius 2.3 cm.
   b) A cone with base radius 3.5 cm and height 5 cm.
   c) A square-based pyramid of base length 4 cm and vertical height 6.5 cm.

Key Words   Hemisphere • Frustum

Pythagoras' Theorem

The Hypotenuse

The **hypotenuse** is:

- the **longest side** on a **right-angled triangle**
- opposite the right angle.

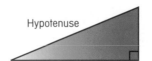

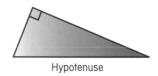

Pythagoras' Theorem

Pythagoras' theorem states that the square on the hypotenuse is equal to the sum of the squares on the other two sides. So, $c^2 = a^2 + b^2$

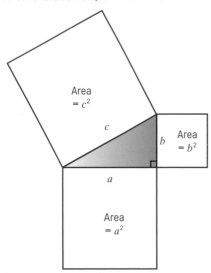

Example

Work out the length of the hypotenuse in this right-angled triangle.

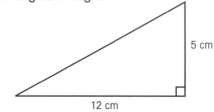

5 cm

12 cm

Solution

Pythagoras' theorem states that $c^2 = a^2 + b^2$

So c^2 is $12^2 + 5^2 = 144 + 25$

$$c^2 = 169$$

So c is $\sqrt{169} = 13$ cm

Pythagorean Triples

A **Pythagorean triple** is where the values of a, b and c are all whole numbers, e.g. (3, 4, 5), (6, 8, 10), (5, 12, 13), (7, 24, 25) and (8, 15, 17).

Example

Work out the area of this isosceles triangle.

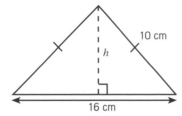

10 cm

h

16 cm

Solution

So $10^2 = h^2 + 8^2$

$100 = h^2 + 64$

$100 - 64 = h^2$

$36 = h^2$

So $h = 6$ cm

Area $= \frac{1}{2} \times 16 \times 6$

Area $= 48$ cm^2

h 10 cm

8 cm

You may have spotted this is a Pythagorean triple. If so, you can just state the height is 6 cm because it's a 6, 8, 10 Pythagorean triple

$\frac{1}{2} \times$ base $\times$ height

Problem Solving

An isosceles triangle can be broken up into two right-angled triangles, so you can use Pythagoras' theorem to work out the height. You then have all the information you need to work out the area.

Key Words   **Hypotenuse** • **Pythagoras' theorem**

Pythagoras' Theorem in 3-D

3-D problems can be broken down into smaller 2-D problems. You should always try to draw diagrams showing right-angled triangles in 2-D because this will make the problem easier.

Example

Work out the length of the diagonal in this cuboid.

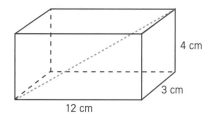

Solution

> **Problem Solving**
>
> You will have to work with other triangles within the shape to obtain the answer.

There are several right-angled triangles in this cuboid.

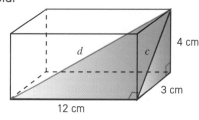

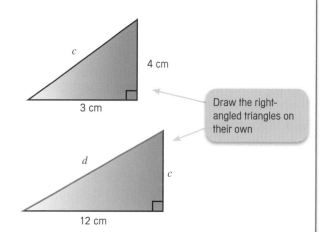

Draw the right-angled triangles on their own

Using the first triangle, this is a Pythagorean triple (3, 4, 5), so $c = 5$ cm

Using the second triangle, this is also a Pythagorean triple (5, 12, 13), so $d = 13$ cm

So the diagonal is 13 cm.

Quick Test

1. Work out the length of the missing sides in these right-angled triangles:

a)

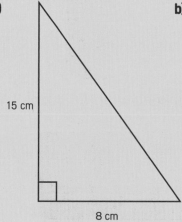

b)

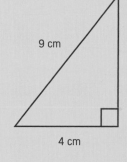

c)

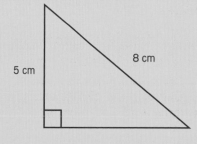

Surface Area

Surface Area and Nets

The **surface area** of a solid:
- is the total area of all the surfaces added together
- is equal to the area of the **net** of the shape.

Cube

The surface area of a cube is the total area of the six squares.

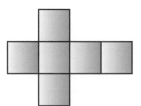

Cuboid

The surface area of a cuboid is the total area of the six faces.

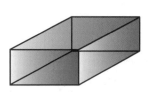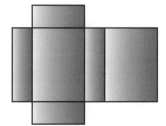

Triangular Prism

The surface area of a triangular prism is the total area of the two triangles and the three rectangles.

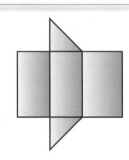

Cylinder

The surface area of a cylinder is the total of the area of the two circles on each end and the **curved surface area**.

The curved surface opens out to form a rectangle with length equal to the circumference of the circular end.

Curved surface area	=	**circumference of end** × **height of cylinder**

$$C = 2\pi r \times h$$

$$C = 2\pi rh$$

Area of one end $= \pi r^2$

Total surface area $= 2\pi rh + 2\pi r^2$

Circumference

Height

Surface area • Net • Curved surface area

Cone

The total surface area of a cone is the total of the area of the circular base and the curved surface area.

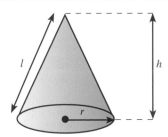

Curved surface area of cone	= π × radius × slant height

$$C = \pi r l$$

Total surface area = $\pi r l + \pi r^2$

N.B. You're given the formula for the curved surface area of a cone in the examination.

Sphere

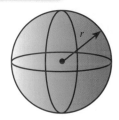

Curved surface area of sphere	= 4 × π × radius²

$$C = 4\pi r^2$$

N.B. You're given the formula for the curved surface area of a sphere in the examination.

Quick Test

1. Work out the total surface area of these shapes:
   a) A cube with edge 3 cm.
   b) A cuboid with edges 5 cm, 3 cm and 2 cm.
   c) A triangular prism with a right-angled triangle cross-section and with base 4 cm, height 3 cm and length 10 cm.
   d) A cylinder with radius 3 cm and height 12 cm. Leave your answer in terms of π.
   e) A cone with radius 3 cm, height 4 cm and slant height 5 cm.

Example 1

Work out the total surface area of this cylinder. Give your answer to 1 decimal place.

4 cm

9 cm

Solution

Area of one end $= \pi r^2$

$= \pi \times 4^2$

$= 50.26\ldots$ cm²

> Remember, do not round values until the last step otherwise your answer may be incorrect

Curved surface area $= 2\pi rh$

$= 2 \times \pi \times 4 \times 9$

$= 226.19\ldots$ cm²

Total surface area $= 2\pi rh + 2\pi r^2$

$= 226.19\ldots + 50.26\ldots + 50.26\ldots$

$= 326.7$ cm²

Example 2

Work out the total surface area of this cone. Give your answer to 1 decimal place.

12 cm

5 cm

Solution

Problem Solving

You're not given the slant height but the sloping side forms a right-angled triangle with the radius and vertical height. This means you can work out the slant height using Pythagorean triples.

Area of base $= \pi r^2$

$= \pi \times 5^2$

$= 78.53\ldots$ cm²

Curved surface area $= \pi r l$

$= \pi \times 5 \times 13$

$= 204.20\ldots$ cm²

> Slant height is 13 cm (5, 12, 13 Pythagorean triple)

Total surface area $= \pi r l + \pi r^2$

$= 204.20\ldots + 78.53\ldots$

$= 282.7$ cm²

Trigonometry in Right-angled Triangles

Labelling Sides and Trigonometrical Ratios

Trigonometry is used to work out unknown lengths or unknown angles in **right-angled triangles**:

- The **hypotenuse** is opposite the right angle.
- The **opposite side** is opposite the marked angle (x).
- The **adjacent side** is next to the marked angle (x).

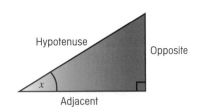

The three trigonometrical ratios you will use are called **sine**, **cosine** and **tangent**. In a right-angled triangle:

$\sin x = \dfrac{\text{opposite}}{\text{hypotenuse}}$	**S** Six	**O** Old	**H** Horses
$\cos x = \dfrac{\text{adjacent}}{\text{hypotenuse}}$	**C** Clumsy	**A** And	**H** Heavy
$\tan x = \dfrac{\text{opposite}}{\text{adjacent}}$	**T** Trod	**O** On	**A** Albert

N.B. You have to remember these for the examination.

Working out a Length and Working out an Angle

To **work out a length** using trigonometry:

1. Label the sides (hyp, opp, adj) in this order.
2. Circle the given side and the one you want to work out.
3. Choose the correct ratio.
4. Set up and solve the equation.

To **work out an angle** using trigonometry:

1. Label the sides (hyp, opp, adj) in this order.
2. Circle the two given sides.
3. Choose the correct ratio.
4. Set up and solve the equation.

Example

Work out the length x.

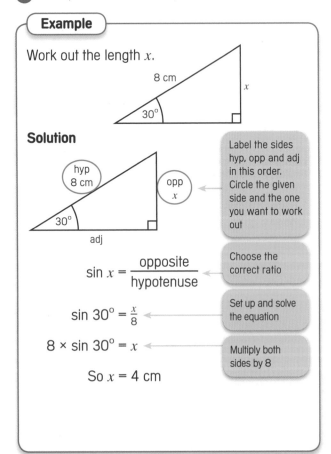

Solution

Label the sides hyp, opp and adj in this order. Circle the given side and the one you want to work out

$$\sin x = \frac{\text{opposite}}{\text{hypotenuse}}$$

Choose the correct ratio

$$\sin 30° = \frac{x}{8}$$

Set up and solve the equation

$$8 \times \sin 30° = x$$

Multiply both sides by 8

$$\text{So } x = 4 \text{ cm}$$

Example

Work out the size of angle x.

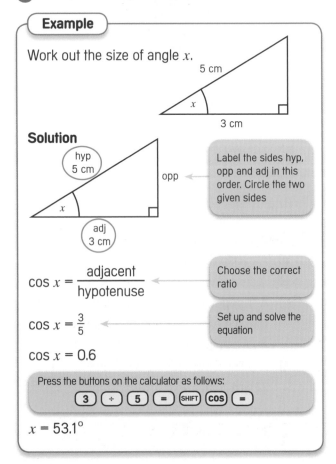

Solution

Label the sides hyp, opp and adj in this order. Circle the two given sides

$$\cos x = \frac{\text{adjacent}}{\text{hypotenuse}}$$

Choose the correct ratio

$$\cos x = \frac{3}{5}$$

Set up and solve the equation

$$\cos x = 0.6$$

Press the buttons on the calculator as follows:

(3) (÷) (5) (=) (SHIFT) (COS) (=)

$$x = 53.1°$$

Key Words   Trigonometry • Hypotenuse • Opposite side • Adjacent side • Sine • Cosine

Trigonometry in Right-angled Triangles

Angles of Elevation and Depression

An **angle of elevation** is the angle measured above a horizontal direction.

An **angle of depression** is the angle measured below a horizontal direction.

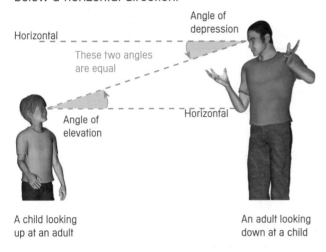

A child looking up at an adult

An adult looking down at a child

Example

A builder stands 5 metres from a building. He is 1.8 metres tall.

Work out the height of the building.

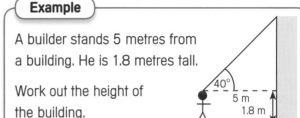

Solution

> **Problem Solving**
>
> Work out the height in the same way that you would find an unknown length in any right-angled triangle but remember to add on the height of the builder.

$$\tan x = \frac{\text{opposite}}{\text{adjacent}}$$

Use x for the height of the triangle

$$\tan 40^\circ = \frac{x}{5}$$

$$5 \times \tan 40^\circ = x$$

Multiply both sides by 5

So $x = 4.2$ m (1 d.p.)

So height of building is $4.2 + 1.8 = 6$ metres

Trigonometry in 3-D

3-D problems can be broken down to make smaller 2-D problems. You should always try to draw diagrams showing right-angled triangles in 2-D as this will make the problem easier.

Quick Test

1. Work out the value of x in each diagram.

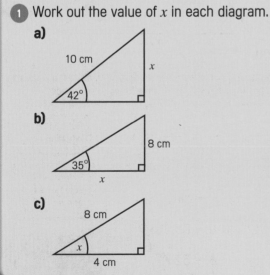

a)

10 cm

x

42°

b)

8 cm

35°

x

c)

8 cm

x

4 cm

Example

The diagram shows a square-based pyramid. The sides of the square are 6 cm. The sloping edges are 5 cm.

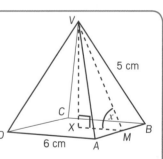

Work out the angle VMX (marked x).

Solution

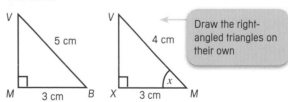

Draw the right-angled triangles on their own

Triangle VBM is a Pythagorean triple, so VM is 4 cm.

Looking at triangle VMX gives $\cos x = \frac{3}{4}$

So $x = 41.4^\circ$

Key Words Tangent • Angle of elevation • Angle of depression

Sine and Cosine Rules

Working out Unknown Lengths and Angles in Triangles

The **sine rule** and **cosine rule** can be used in a triangle to work out:

- an unknown length
- an unknown angle.

If a triangle has vertices A, B and C, then the sides opposite each angle are a, b and c respectively.

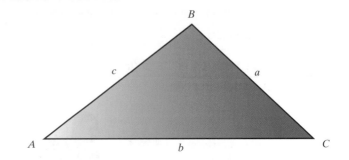

Sine Rule

This is the sine rule:

$$\frac{a}{\sin A} = \frac{b}{\sin B} = \frac{c}{\sin C}$$

N.B. You're given this in the examination.

The equation can also be used 'upside down', i.e.

$$\frac{\sin A}{a} = \frac{\sin B}{b} = \frac{\sin C}{c}$$

The sine rule can be used when you know both values for a particular letter (e.g. A and a) together with one other value. So you could use the sine rule if you knew A, a and b or A, a and C.

To use the sine rule:

1. label the sides
2. write out the formula
3. circle the parts you know
4. set up and solve the equation.

Example 1

Work out the length of AC in this triangle.

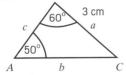

Solution

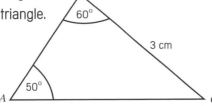

Label the sides. In this triangle $a = 3$ cm, $A = 50°$, $B = 60°$

Write out the formula and circle the known parts

$\frac{c}{\sin C}$ isn't used here

$$\frac{(a)}{(\sin A)} = \frac{b}{(\sin B)} = \frac{c}{\sin C}$$

So $\dfrac{3}{\sin 50°} = \dfrac{b}{\sin 60°}$

Set up the equation

$\dfrac{3 \times \sin 60°}{\sin 50°} = b$

Multiply both sides by sin 60°

So b (side AC) = 3.4 cm

Example 2

Work out the size of angle B in this triangle.

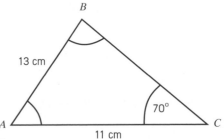

Solution

Label the sides, then write out the formula and circle the known parts. Then identify which part of the formula isn't needed

So $\dfrac{11}{\sin B} = \dfrac{13}{\sin 70°}$

Set up the equation

$11 \times \sin 70° = 13 \times \sin B$

Multiply both sides by sin B and sin 70°

$\dfrac{11 \times \sin 70°}{13} = \sin B$

So $\sin B = 0.795...$

Divide both sides by 13

$B = 52.7°$

Sine and Cosine Rules

Cosine Rule

This is the cosine rule:

$$a^2 = b^2 + c^2 - 2bc \cos A$$

N.B. You're given this in the examination.

This can be rearranged to:

$$\cos A = \frac{b^2 + c^2 - a^2}{2bc}$$

N.B. You're **not** given this in the examination.

The cosine rule can be used when you know two sides and the angle between them, e.g. b, c and A, or when you know all three sides, i.e. a, b and c.

To use the cosine rule:

1. label the sides
2. write out the formula
3. circle the parts you know
4. set up and solve the equation.

N.B. It's easier to use the labels b, c and A to match the formula given.

Example 1

Work out the length of BC in this triangle.

Solution

Label the sides. In this triangle $b = 6$ cm, $c = 8$ cm, $A = 34°$

Write out the formula

$$a^2 = b^2 + c^2 - 2bc \cos A$$

So $a^2 = 6^2 + 8^2 - (2 \times 6 \times 8 \cos 34°)$

Set up the equation

$$a^2 = 20.4...$$

a = the square root of 20.4...

So a (side BC) = 4.52 cm

Quick Test

1. Work out x in each part.

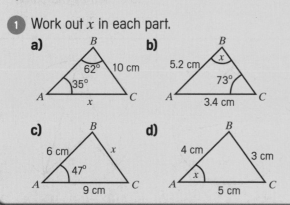

a)
b)
c)
d)

Example 2

Look at the triangle.

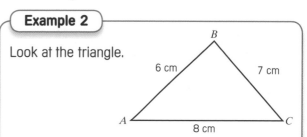

a) Work out the size of angle A.

Solution

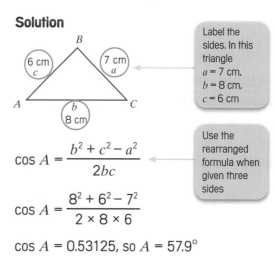

Label the sides. In this triangle $a = 7$ cm, $b = 8$ cm, $c = 6$ cm

Use the rearranged formula when given three sides

$$\cos A = \frac{b^2 + c^2 - a^2}{2bc}$$

$$\cos A = \frac{8^2 + 6^2 - 7^2}{2 \times 8 \times 6}$$

$\cos A = 0.53125$, so $A = 57.9°$

b) Which angle is the biggest? Give a reason for your answer.

Solution

Problem Solving

In any triangle, the biggest angle is always opposite the longest side and the smallest angle is always opposite the shortest side.

Angle B is biggest because b (side AC) is the longest side.

Circle Theorems

Tangents

A **tangent** is a straight line that touches the circle at a point on the circumference. Here are some properties relating to tangents of circles:

- The angle between a tangent and the radius at the point on the circumference is 90°.
- Tangents to a circle drawn from the same point are equal in length.
- The triangles formed using tangents from a common point, radii and a line drawn from the centre are **congruent** right-angled triangles.

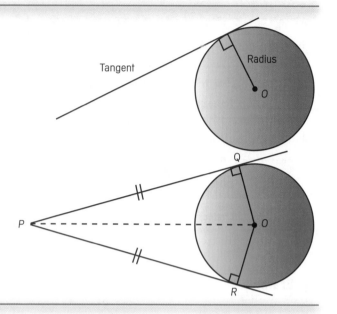

Chords

A radius drawn **perpendicular** (at 90°) to a chord bisects the chord.

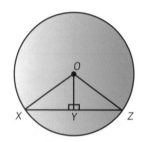

Triangle *OXZ* is isosceles

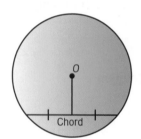

Circle Theorems

Basic Circle Theorems

You need to know these basic circle theorems:

This diagram shows an angle x **subtended** by an arc.	The angle at the centre of a circle is twice the angle at the circumference that is subtended by the same arc.	Any angle at the circumference that is subtended by a diameter is 90°.	Angles at the circumference, in the same segment and subtended by the same arc, are equal.

Key Words   **Tangent • Congruent • Perpendicular • Subtend**

Cyclic Quadrilaterals

A **cyclic quadrilateral** is a quadrilateral with all four vertices on the circumference of a circle.

Opposite angles of a cyclic quadrilateral add up to 180°.

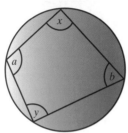

$x + y = 180°$

$a + b = 180°$

Alternate Segment Theorem

The angle between a tangent and a chord through the point of contact is equal to the angle at the circumference in the **alternate segment**, subtended by the chord.

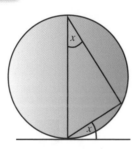

Quick Test

1. Work out the value of the lettered angle in each part.

a)

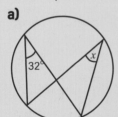

b)

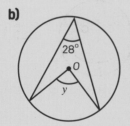

c)

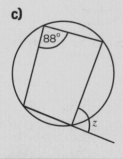

d)

Example 1

Work out the size of x.

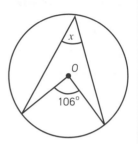

Solution

The angle at the centre is twice the angle at the circumference.

So x is $\dfrac{106°}{2} = 53°$

Example 2

Work out the size of y.

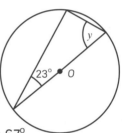

Solution

Angle at circumference = 90°

So y is $180° - 90° - 23° = 67°$

Example 3

Work out the size of z.

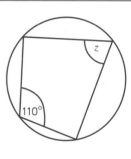

Solution

Opposite angles of a cyclic quadrilateral add up to 180°.

So z is $180° - 110° = 70°$

Example 4

Work out the size of x and the size of y.

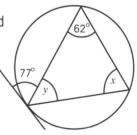

Solution

$x = 77°$ ← Alternate segment theorem

So y is $180° - 62° - 77° = 41°$

Transformations

A **transformation** changes the appearance of a shape. It may change the shape's **position**, **size** or **orientation**.

You'll need to draw or describe **reflections**, **rotations**, **translations** and **enlargements** of 2-D shapes. The original shape is called the **object**. The transformed shape is called the **image**.

Reflections

A **reflection** transforms a shape so that it's a **mirror image** of the original shape. The object and the image have line symmetry.

To describe a reflection you have to state the position of the mirror line, e.g. a reflection in the x-axis or a reflection in the line $x = 2$

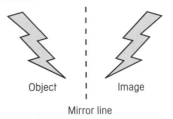

Object ┆ Image

Mirror line

Each point on the object is the same distance from the mirror line as its corresponding point on the image

Rotations

A **rotation** transforms a shape so that the original shape is **turned about** a fixed point. The fixed point is called the **centre of rotation**.

To describe a rotation you have to state:
- the angle turned with the direction of turn (clockwise or anticlockwise)
- the centre of rotation.

For example, a rotation 90° clockwise about (0, 0) or a rotation 180° about (3, 2).

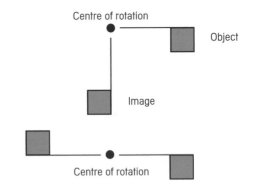

Centre of rotation

Object

Image

Centre of rotation

Each point on the object is the same distance from the centre of rotation as its corresponding point on the image

Translations

A **translation** transforms a shape so that the original shape **moves** without reflecting or rotating.

To describe a translation you have to state:
- the distance moved horizontally
- the distance moved vertically.

This can be written in words, e.g. 3 units to the right and 2 units down, or 4 units to the left and 5 units up.

Translations can also be written as **vectors**, e.g. $\binom{3}{-2}$ and $\binom{-4}{5}$:
- The top number is the horizontal movement (right is positive and left is negative).
- The bottom number is the vertical movement (up is positive and down is negative).

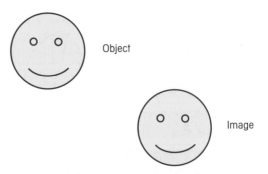

Object

Image

Every point in the shape moves in the same direction and through the same distance

Enlargements

An **enlargement** transforms a shape so that the original shape **increases** or **decreases** in size. The **scale factor** of an enlargement shows how the lengths of a shape increase or decrease, e.g. for a scale factor 2, the lengths double.

To describe an enlargement you have to state:
- the centre of enlargement
- the scale factor of the enlargement.

For example, an enlargement, centre (0, 0), scale factor 2.

A **fractional scale factor** means the image will be **smaller** than the object.

A **negative scale factor** means the image will be on the **opposite side** of the centre of enlargement to the original shape.

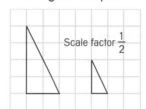

Scale factor $\frac{1}{2}$

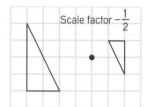

Scale factor $-\frac{1}{2}$

Example 1

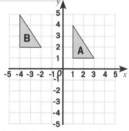

a) Describe the single transformation that takes triangle A to triangle B.

Solution

Translation 5 units to the left and 1 unit up or translation $\begin{pmatrix} -5 \\ 1 \end{pmatrix}$

b) Reflect triangle A in the line $y = -x$. Label it C.

Solution

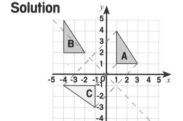

Example 2

Enlarge triangle A with scale factor 2 and centre of enlargement (0, 1). Label it B.

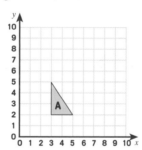

Solution

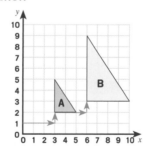

Example 3

Triangle A is translated $\begin{pmatrix} -5 \\ 0 \end{pmatrix}$ to form triangle B. Triangle B is then rotated 180° about the origin to form triangle C. Describe the single transformation that takes triangle A to triangle C.

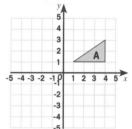

Solution

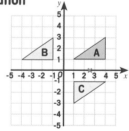

Triangle A to triangle C is a rotation of 180° about (2.5, 0).

Quick Test

1 Describe the single transformation that takes:
   a) triangle A to triangle B
   b) triangle A to triangle C
   c) triangle A to triangle D.

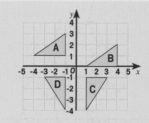

Congruency and Similarity

Congruent Shapes

Two shapes are **congruent** if they're the **same size** and the **same shape**.

When shapes are reflected, rotated or translated, the image is congruent to the object.

All these shapes are congruent:

Congruent Triangles

Corresponding sides in two triangles are sides in the same position or opposite the same angle.

Two triangles are congruent if they satisfy any one of the following four conditions:

Side, Side, Side (SSS)	Side, Angle, Side (SAS)	Angle, Angle, Corresponding Side (AA corr S)	Right angle, Hypotenuse, Side (RHS)
All three sides of one triangle are equal to the three sides in the other triangle.	Two sides and the included angle of one triangle are equal to the two sides and the included angle in the other triangle.	Two angles and a corresponding side of one triangle are equal to two angles and a corresponding side of the other triangle.	Both triangles have a right angle, an equal hypotenuse and another equal side.
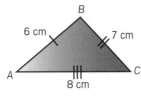 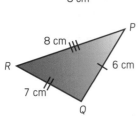	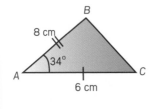 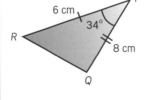	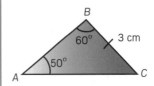 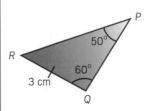	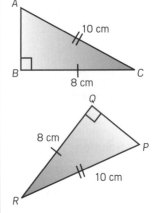
$AB = PQ$, $BC = QR$, $AC = PR$, so congruent (SSS).	$AB = PQ$, $AC = PR$, angle A = angle P, so congruent (SAS).	Angle A = angle P, angle B = angle Q, $BC = QR$, so congruent (AA corr S).	Angle B = angle Q, $AC = PR$, $BC = QR$, so congruent (RHS).

Example

Prove that triangles *ABC* and *PQR* are congruent.

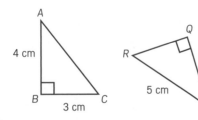

Solution

Problem Solving

Look at the information you are given – these are right-angled triangles with one equal side. You can use Pythagoras' theorem to find the hypotenuse of triangle *ABC* and see if they match to satisfy RHS.

Using Pythagorean triples in triangle *ABC*, $AC = 5$ cm

Angle B = Angle Q = $90°$ (right angle)

$AC = PR = 5$ cm (hypotenuse)

$AB = PQ = 4$ cm (side)

So the triangles are congruent (RHS).

Similar Shapes

Two shapes are **similar** if one shape is an enlargement of the other:

- The angles in one shape will be equal to the corresponding angles in the other shape.
- The corresponding sides of each shape are in the same ratio.

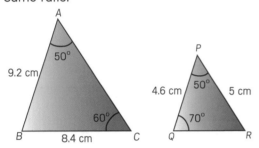

The angles in both triangles are 50°, 60° and 70° so the triangles are similar.

The lengths on triangle *ABC* are twice the corresponding lengths on triangle *PQR* as 9.2 cm = 2 × 4.6 cm

So $\frac{AB}{PQ} = \frac{BC}{QR} = \frac{AC}{PR}$

$\frac{9.2}{4.6} = \frac{8.4}{QR} = \frac{AC}{5}$

$2 = \frac{8.4}{QR}$ and $2 = \frac{AC}{5}$

So *QR* = 4.2 cm and *AC* = 10 cm

Example 1

Triangles *ABC* and *PQR* are similar. Work out the length of *PR*.

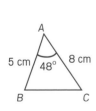 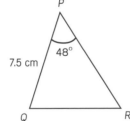

Solution A

$\frac{AB}{PQ} = \frac{AC}{PR}$

$\frac{5}{7.5} = \frac{8}{PR}$

$PR = \frac{8 \times 7.5}{5}$ ← Rearranging

$PR = 12$ cm

Solution B

PQ is 1.5 times *AB*.
So *PR* is *AC* × 1.5
= 12 cm

Areas and Volumes

When 2-D or 3-D shapes are similar and their corresponding lengths are in the ratio $x : y$

- **Area ratio** = $x^2 : y^2$
- **Volume ratio** = $x^3 : y^3$

Example 2

Cuboid A is similar to cuboid B.

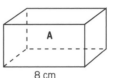

Write down the ratio of their surface areas and the ratio of their volumes.

Solution

The ratio of length is 8 : 4 = 2 : 1

So the ratio of the surface areas is $2^2 : 1^2 = 4 : 1$

The ratio of volumes is $2^3 : 1^3 = 8 : 1$

Quick Test

1. Why are these triangles congruent?

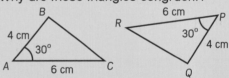

2. In the diagram *BC* is parallel to *DE*.

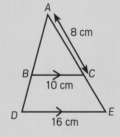

Work out the length of *CE*.

3. The radii of two spheres are 6 cm and 9 cm.
Write down the ratio of their volumes in its simplest form.

Vectors

A **vector** is a quantity that has both **magnitude** (size) and **direction**. Examples of vectors are velocity and force.

Vectors are usually represented by a line with an arrow on it. The vector may be labelled:
- at each end with capital letters
- with a small letter (printed in bold type but handwritten as $\underline{a}$).

For example, here $\overrightarrow{AB}$ = **a**

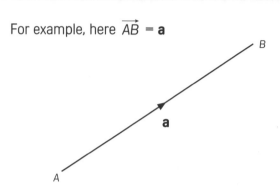

Adding and Subtracting Vectors

To add two vectors, you can draw them so that they join up. So if **a** represents the vector $\binom{4}{3}$ and **b** represents the vector $\binom{3}{-1}$, the **resultant a + b** is:

$$\binom{4}{3} + \binom{3}{-1} = \binom{7}{2}$$

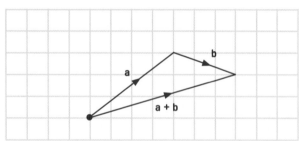

To subtract a vector is to reverse the direction, so
a − b is $\binom{4}{3} - \binom{3}{-1} = \binom{1}{4}$

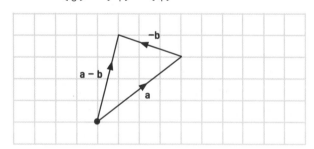

We can also write $\overrightarrow{AB} + \overrightarrow{BC} = \overrightarrow{AC}$ because translating from A to B and then B to C is equivalent to A to C.

Example

A is the point $(1, 2)$. $\overrightarrow{AB} = \binom{5}{-3}$. Work out the coordinates of B.

Solution

Problem Solving

Use a grid to work out the solution to this type of question.

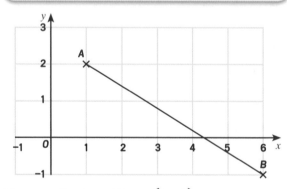

The coordinates of B are $(6, -1)$

Key Words   **Vector • Magnitude • Direction**

Multiples of Vectors

A vector that is a multiple of another vector is:

- in the same direction (parallel or in the same line)
- bigger (or smaller) by the same factor as the multiple.

For example if $\vec{AB} = \mathbf{a} + 4\mathbf{b}$ and $\vec{CD} = 2\mathbf{a} + 8\mathbf{b}$, then $\vec{CD} = 2 \times \vec{AB}$. This means:

- $\vec{CD}$ is in the same direction as $\vec{AB}$
- $\vec{CD}$ is twice the size of $\vec{AB}$.

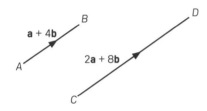

If $\vec{PQ} = 2\mathbf{a} - 3\mathbf{b}$ and $\vec{PR} = 6\mathbf{a} - 9\mathbf{b}$, then $\vec{PR} = 3 \times \vec{PQ}$. This means:

- $\vec{PR}$ is three times the size of $\vec{PQ}$
- as $\vec{PQ}$ and $\vec{PR}$ both pass through P in the same direction, P, Q and R are in the same straight line. This is called **collinear**.

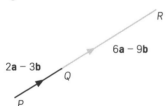

Quick Test

1. $\vec{OA} = \mathbf{a}$, $\vec{OB} = \mathbf{b}$, $\vec{OC} = 2\mathbf{a} - 3\mathbf{b}$
   Work out the following vectors.
   a) $\vec{BA}$
   b) $\vec{AC}$
   c) $\vec{CB}$

2. Work out:
   a) $\binom{5}{-2} + \binom{-3}{4}$
   b) $\binom{1}{0} - \binom{2}{-4}$

Example

In triangle OAB, $\vec{OA} = \mathbf{a}$, $\vec{OB} = \mathbf{b}$. The point X divides the line AB in the ratio $2 : 1$

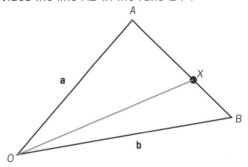

a) Work out the vector $\vec{AB}$ in terms of $\mathbf{a}$ and $\mathbf{b}$.

Solution
$\vec{AB} = \vec{AO} + \vec{OB}$
$\vec{AB} = -\mathbf{a} + \mathbf{b}$

b) Work out the vector $\vec{OX}$ in terms of $\mathbf{a}$ and $\mathbf{b}$.

Solution
$\vec{AX} = \frac{2}{3}\vec{AB}$

$\vec{AX} = -\frac{2}{3}\mathbf{a} + \frac{2}{3}\mathbf{b}$

$\vec{OX} = \vec{OA} + \vec{AX}$

$\vec{OX} = \mathbf{a} - \frac{2}{3}\mathbf{a} + \frac{2}{3}\mathbf{b}$

$\vec{OX} = \frac{1}{3}\mathbf{a} + \frac{2}{3}\mathbf{b}$

c) $\vec{OC} = \mathbf{a} + 2\mathbf{b}$. What can you say about the points O, X and C?

Solution
$\vec{OC} = \mathbf{a} + 2\mathbf{b}$

So $\vec{OC} = 3\vec{OX}$ ← Remember that if a vector is a multiple of another vector, they are in the same direction

So O, C and X are collinear and X divides OC in the ratio $1 : 2$

Conversions, Bearings and Scale Drawings

Conversions

For the examination you need to learn these **conversions** from **metric** to **imperial** measurements:

- 1 kg ≈ 2.2 pounds
- 4.5 litres ≈ 1 gallon
- 8 km ≈ 5 miles
- 2.5 cm ≈ 1 inch

You should also know common metric conversions:

Length	1 m = 100 cm
	1 km = 1000 m
	1 m = 1000 mm
	1 cm = 10 mm
Mass	1 tonne = 1000 kg
	1 kg = 1000 g

Example 1

Convert 56 km to miles.

Solution

8 km ≈ 5 miles

So 1 km ≈ $\frac{5}{8}$ mile ← Divide by 8

56 km is $\frac{5}{8}$ × 56 = 35 miles ← Multiply by 56

Example 2

Use the graph to convert:

a) 16 gallons into litres

b) 40 litres to gallons.

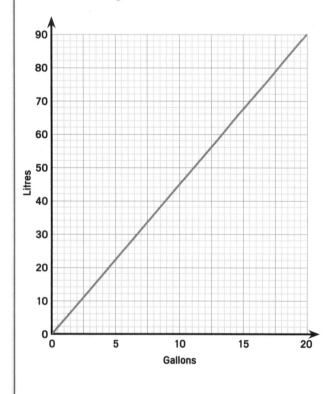

Solution

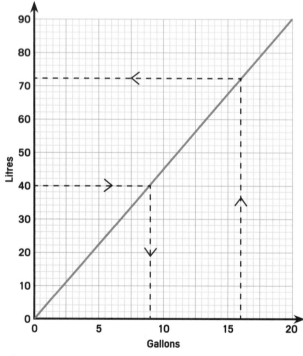

a) 16 gallons ≈ 72 litres

b) 40 litres ≈ 9 gallons

Conversions, Bearings and Scale Drawings

Bearings and Scale Drawings

A **bearing** gives the direction to one place from another.

To measure a **three-figure bearing**:
- start from North
- measure clockwise

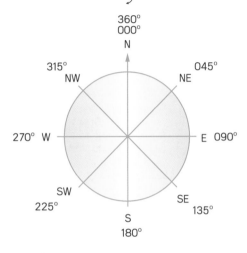

Three-figure bearings should always be given using three digits, e.g. a bearing of 45° is written 045°.

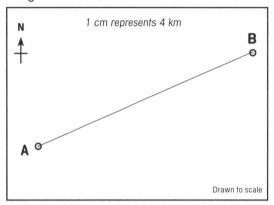
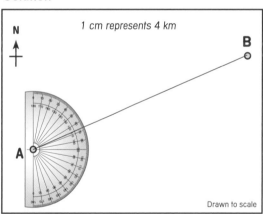
Quick Test

1 Sketch bearings of:
   a) 030°   **b)** 140°   **c)** 270°

Constructions

Accurate Drawings

A **construction** is an accurate drawing using a combination of ruler, protractor and a pair of compasses. In your examination it's important that when you use a pair of compasses, the construction arcs are clearly shown and that all lengths and angles are accurate.

Example 1

a) Construct triangle ABC with AB = 3 cm, BC = 2.5 cm and AC = 2 cm

Solution

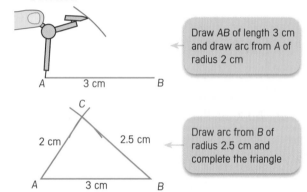

Draw AB of length 3 cm and draw arc from A of radius 2 cm

Draw arc from B of radius 2.5 cm and complete the triangle

b) Construct triangle ABC with AB = 3 cm, AC = 2 cm and angle BAC = 70°

Solution

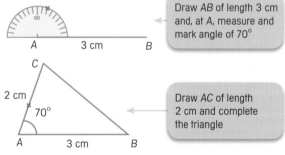

Draw AB of length 3 cm and, at A, measure and mark angle of 70°

Draw AC of length 2 cm and complete the triangle

c) Construct triangle ABC with AB = 2 cm, AC = 2 cm and angle ABC = 50°

Solution

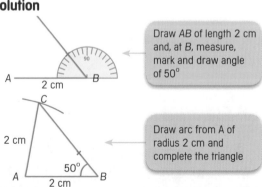

Draw AB of length 2 cm and, at B, measure, mark and draw angle of 50°

Draw arc from A of radius 2 cm and complete the triangle

Example 2

a) Use a ruler and a pair of compasses only to construct an angle of 60°.

Solution

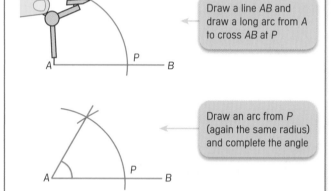

Draw a line AB and draw a long arc from A to cross AB at P

Draw an arc from P (again the same radius) and complete the angle

b) Use a ruler and a pair of compasses only to construct an angle of 90°.

Solution

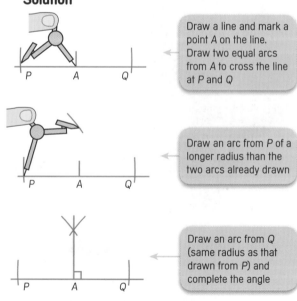

Draw a line and mark a point A on the line. Draw two equal arcs from A to cross the line at P and Q

Draw an arc from P of a longer radius than the two arcs already drawn

Draw an arc from Q (same radius as that drawn from P) and complete the angle

Example 3

a) Draw a line *AB*. Construct the **perpendicular bisector** of the line *AB*.

Solution

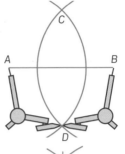

Draw a line *AB*. Draw long arcs of equal radius from points *A* and *B* to intersect at points *C* and *D*

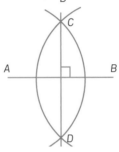

Join *CD* to form the perpendicular bisector

b) Draw a line *AB*. Construct a perpendicular from a point *O* above the line.

Solution

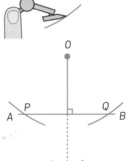

Draw a line *AB*. Draw two arcs from *O* to cross *AB* at *P* and *Q*, then draw an arc from *P*

Draw an arc from *Q* using the same radius as that used for the arc from *P* and complete the perpendicular

c) Draw an angle. Construct the angle bisector.

Solution

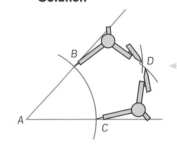

Draw an angle at point *A*. Draw a long arc from *A* to cut the lines at *B* and *C*. Draw arcs of equal radius from points *B* and *C* to intersect at point *D*

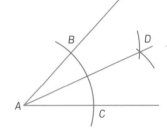

Join *A* to *D* to form the bisector of the angle

d) Construct an angle of 30°.

Solution

Problem Solving
Think about how you can combine basic constructions. In this case, construct an angle of 60° and then bisect it to create an angle half the size.

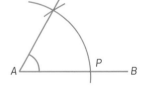

Construct the angle of 60°

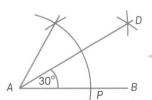

Bisect the angle of 60°

Quick Test

1. Construct a triangle *ABC* with *AB* = 8 cm, *BC* = 6.5 cm and *AC* = 5.7 cm
2. Construct an angle of 45°.

Loci and 3-D Coordinates

Loci

A **locus** (plural: **loci**) is a path made by a set of points that follow a rule.

Here are some facts about loci:

The locus of points that are a fixed distance from a fixed point is a circle. 	The locus of points that are a fixed distance from a fixed line is a pair of parallel lines with a semicircle at either end. 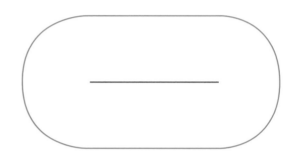
The locus of points that are a fixed distance from two fixed points is the perpendicular bisector of the line joining the points. 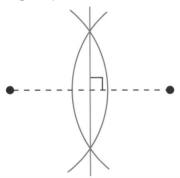	The locus of points that are a fixed distance from two fixed lines is the angle bisector of the two lines. 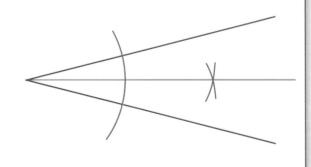

Example

A goat is tied to the corner of a building by a rope 5 metres long. Show the area that the goat can reach on the diagram.

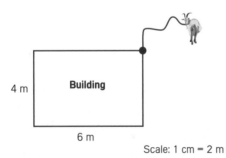

Scale: 1 cm = 2 m

Solution

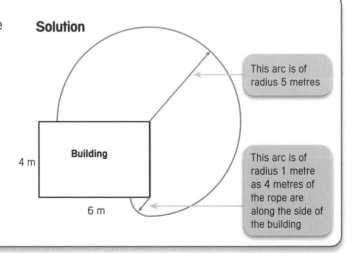

This arc is of radius 5 metres

This arc is of radius 1 metre as 4 metres of the rope are along the side of the building

3-D Coordinates

You need to know that:

- **2-D coordinates** are used to identify points in a plane, using x and y-axes
- **3-D coordinates** are used to identify points in space, using x, y and z-axes.

The axes are drawn at right angles to each other as shown.

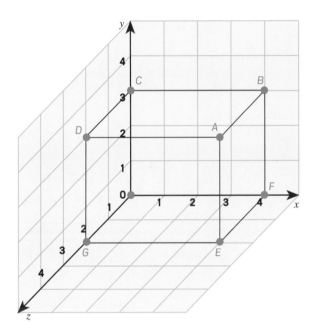

A has coordinates (4, 3, 2) because it's 4 units on the x-axis, 3 units on the y-axis and 2 units on the z-axis.

C has coordinates (0, 3, 0) because it's 0 units on the x-axis, 3 units on the y-axis and 0 units on the z-axis.

E has coordinates (4, 0, 2) because it's 4 units on the x-axis, 0 units on the y-axis and 2 units on the z-axis.

Quick Test

1. A goat is tied to a post in each field by a rope 5 metres long. In each case describe or draw the locus of the shape the goat can reach. On the diagrams, 1 cm = 2 m

a)

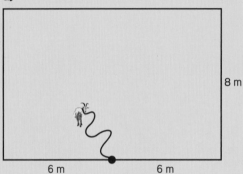

6 m   6 m   8 m

b)

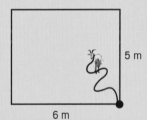

6 m   5 m

c)

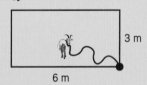

6 m   3 m

2. Look again at the diagram for 3-D coordinates on the left of this page and write down the coordinates of:

a) F

b) B

c) G

d) D

Exam Practice Questions

You may wish to answer these questions on a separate piece of paper so that you can show full working out, which you will be expected to do in the exam.

Questions labelled with an asterisk (*) are ones where the quality of your written communication (QWC) will be assessed.

1. Work out the area of the trapezium.

    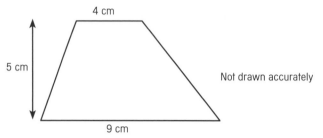

    Not drawn accurately

    (2 marks)

2.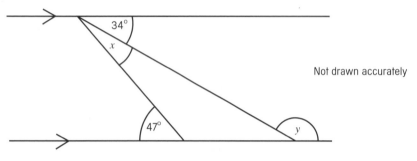

    Not drawn accurately

    a) Work out the value of x.

    (2 marks)

    b) Work out the value of y.

    (2 marks)

3. Work out the area of a circle of radius 4 cm. Give your answer in cm^2 to 1 decimal place.

    (3 marks)

4. A ship sails 20 miles north from a port (P) to a lighthouse (L).

    It then turns and sails 25 miles east to an oil rig (R). It then returns directly to the port.

    a) Make a sketch of the route sailed by the ship.

    (2 marks)

b) Work out the distance from the oil rig back to the port. Give your answer to a suitable degree of accuracy.

_____ *(3 marks)*

 5.

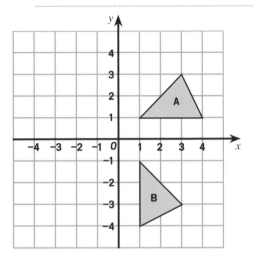

Describe fully the **single** transformation that maps triangle A to triangle B.

_____ *(3 marks)*

 6. Construct a triangle ABC with AB = 3 cm, angle BAC = 50° and angle ABC = 30°   *(3 marks)*

7. The diagram shows a solid metal cylinder and an open cuboid.

The cylinder is melted down and the metal is poured into the cuboid.

Work out the height of the metal in the cuboid.

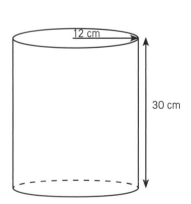

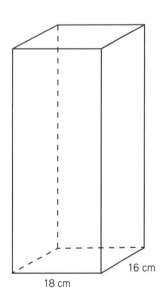

_____ *(5 marks)*

*8. A, B and D are points on the circumference of the circle.

Triangle BCD is isosceles.

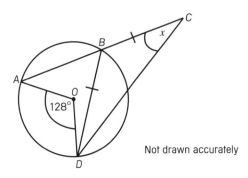

Not drawn accurately

Work out the value of x. Give reasons for your answer.

....

.... **(5 marks)**

*9. Work out the size of the smallest angle in this triangle.

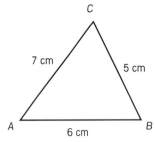

Not drawn accurately

.... **(4 marks)**

10. Work out the length of BC.

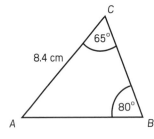

Not drawn accurately

.... **(4 marks)**

11. The diagram shows a rectangle. The area is 27 cm².

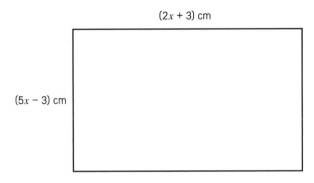

$(2x + 3)$ cm

$(5x - 3)$ cm

Not drawn accurately

a) Show that $10x^2 + 9x - 36 = 0$

....

.... *(3 marks)*

b) Solve the quadratic equation $10x^2 + 9x - 36 = 0$

.... *(3 marks)*

c) Work out the length of the longest side of the rectangle.

.... *(1 mark)*

 12. Give a reason why this pair of triangles is congruent.

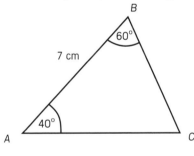

B

$60°$

7 cm

$40°$

A C

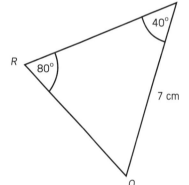

P

$40°$

R $80°$

7 cm

Q Not drawn accurately

.... *(1 mark)*

Handling Data Cycle and Questionnaires

The Handling Data Cycle

Statistics is about the collection, organisation and interpretation of **data**.

A **hypothesis** is an idea or assumption which is then tested to decide whether it's true or false. To test a hypothesis the **handling data cycle** is used.

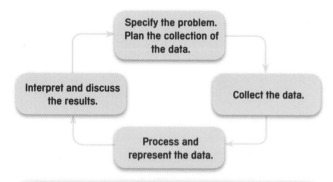

Specify the problem. Plan the collection of the data.

Collect the data.

Process and represent the data.

Interpret and discuss the results.

To use the handling data cycle:

* state a hypothesis, outlining the problem and planning the task
* plan the data collection and collect the data
* process the data using statistical calculations, e.g. mean and range (see page 92)
* interpret the data and make conclusions.

The final step includes reviewing the task, refining it and continuing the cycle if necessary.

Data Collection

You need to know these terms:

* **Primary data** is data that you collect.
* **Secondary data** is data that has already been collected by someone else.
* **Discrete data** can only have certain values in a given range, e.g. number of goals scored: 0, 1, 2, 3, and so on. It's not possible to have half a goal!
* **Continuous data** can have any value within a given range, e.g. height of a person: 1.83… metres.
* **Qualitative data** is data that is non-numerical, e.g. colour of cars.
* **Quantitative data** is data that is numerical, e.g. number of cars.
* A **survey** is an organised way of collecting data.

* A **questionnaire** is one way of carrying out a survey.
* **Observations** in an **experiment** are another way of carrying out a survey.
* A **population** is all the group you're investigating.
* A **sample** is a part of the population you're investigating.

To collect the data:
1. decide whether to use the population or a sample
2. carry out a survey or an experiment
3. record the results in a suitable way, e.g. use a tally chart or a frequency table.

Processing and Representing the Data

To process and represent the data:

* a suitable average could be calculated (mode, median or mean)
* a suitable measure of spread could be calculated (range or interquartile range)
* suitable statistical charts, diagrams or graphs could be drawn.

Handling Data Cycle and Questionnaires

Interpreting and Discussing Results

Results are interpreted and discussed in order to:
- make comparisons
- draw conclusions
- decide whether the hypothesis is true, not true or inconclusive
- decide whether to refine the hypothesis or continue with the cycle.

Example

A farmer wants to compare two types of lettuce, A and B, to decide which is better. Describe the handling data cycle that he could use.

Solution

Problem Solving

Think about what he would want to know and how he would collect the data. Then set out the information in a logical way.

State a hypothesis:

Lettuce A grows faster than lettuce B.

Plan the data collection and collect the data:

Plant a tray of each seed and store in the same conditions to avoid **bias**.

After two weeks measure the plants and record the results.

Process and represent the data:
- Work out the mean height of lettuces in each tray.
- Work out the interquartile range of the heights of lettuces in each tray.

Interpret and discuss the results:
- Look at the results and compare the means and the interquartile ranges.
- Decide whether there are any significant differences by referring to the context of the hypothesis.
- State how to improve the cycle, e.g. use a larger sample of seeds or measure after a different period of time.

Questionnaires

Any question written as part of a questionnaire for a survey should:
- be as simple as possible
- allow anyone asked to give an answer
- have responses that don't overlap and have no gaps
- not be a leading, personal or irrelevant question.

Quick Test

1. Ali thinks that boys are better than girls at spelling in his class. How could he use the handling data cycle to test his hypothesis?
2. Criticise this question:
   Do you agree that fast food is bad for you?
   ❏ Yes ❏ No

Example

Here is a question from a questionnaire about eating out. Give two criticisms of the response section.

How many times do you eat out each week?
❏ 1–3 ❏ 3–6 ❏ More than 7

Solution

3 could be in the first or second box. → Response options overlap

It's not possible to answer 0 or 7 times. → Gaps in the response options

Averages and Range

Mode, Median, Mean and Range

An **average** is a measure used to represent a set of data. The most commonly used averages are:

- the **mode** – the most common value (**MO**de is **MO**st)
- the **median** – the middle value of the ordered data or halfway between the middle two values for an even number of values (**MeD**ian is **MiD**dle)
- **mean** – given by the formula:

$$\text{Mean} = \frac{\text{sum of the values}}{\text{number of values}}$$

(Me**AN** is add up **AN**d divide.)

The **range** measures the spread of the data.

$$\text{Range} = \text{biggest value} - \text{smallest value}$$

Example

Find five numbers that have a range of 6 and a mean of 4.

Solution

> **Problem Solving**
>
> Work out the sum of the numbers using the mean. Here the sum of the numbers is five times the mean as there are five numbers.

Sum of the numbers is $4 \times 5 = 20$

Written in order the first and last numbers have a difference of 6.

2 … … … 8 ←

> Trying 2 and 8 means the other three numbers add up to 10

So 2 3 3 4 8 works. ←

> There are lots of other answers. Can you find a different answer?

Mode, Median, Mean and Range from a Frequency Table

The mode, median, mean and range can be worked out from a frequency table.

Example

Work out the mode, median, mean and range of the number of children per family.

Number of Children (x)	Frequency (f)	Frequency × Number of Children (fx)
0	4	0
1	6	6
2	9	18
3	1	3
	Total = 20	Total = 27

Solution

The mode is the most common, which is 2 children per family.

The median is the middle of the 20 values, which is halfway between the 10th and 11th values.

> Listing in order: 0, 0, 0, 0, 1, 1, 1, 1, 1,(1, 2,)2, 2, 2, 2, 2, 2, 2, 2, 3

10th value = 1, 11th value = 2, so median = 1.5 children per family

$$\text{Mean} = \frac{\text{sum of the values}}{\text{number of values}}$$

Mean = $\frac{27}{20}$ = 1.35 children per family

Range is $3 - 0 = 3$ children per family

Grouped Data

The **modal class** is the class with the biggest frequency. The class containing the median is the class that contains the middle value. To estimate the mean, mid-values are used to represent each class.

Recorded Temp., T (°C)	Frequency (f)	Mid-Temp. Values (x)	Frequency × Mid-Temp. Values (fx)
$10 \leqslant T < 15$	2	12.5	$2 \times 12.5 = 25$
$15 \leqslant T < 20$	4	17.5	$4 \times 17.5 = 70$
$20 \leqslant T < 25$	5	22.5	$5 \times 22.5 = 112.5$
$25 \leqslant T < 30$	8	27.5	$8 \times 27.5 = 220$
$30 \leqslant T < 35$	5	32.5	$5 \times 32.5 = 162.5$
	Total = 24		**Total = 590**

These are class intervals

These are halfway values for the class intervals

a) Work out the modal class, the class that contains the median and an estimate of the mean for the recorded temperatures.

Solution

The modal class is $25°C \leqslant T < 30°C$

There are 24 temperatures altogether so the middle is halfway between the 12th and 13th temperatures.

The class containing these is $25°C \leqslant T < 30°C$

The individual temperatures aren't known so the mid-value of each group is used as an estimate.

Estimate of mean = $\dfrac{\text{total of recorded temperatures}}{\text{total frequency}}$

Estimate of mean is $\dfrac{590}{24} = 24.58°C$

b) Explain why it's not possible to work out the range.

Solution

Problem Solving

Think about what you need to know to work out the range and what information is missing. Write your explanation clearly.

The lowest and highest temperatures aren't known, only that the lowest temperature is in the class $10°C \leqslant T < 15°C$ and the highest temperature is in the class $30°C \leqslant T < 35°C$.

Quick Test

1 Work out the mode, median, mean and range for this data.

x	f
3	1
4	9
5	6
6	4

2 Work out the modal class, the class that contains the median and an estimate of the mean for this data.

x	f
$0 < x \leqslant 2$	10
$2 < x \leqslant 4$	21
$4 < x \leqslant 6$	13
$6 < x \leqslant 8$	7

Sorting Data and Sampling Methods

Stem-and-Leaf Diagrams

A **stem-and-leaf diagram** is used to sort discrete data into **ordered** groups. Numbers in the **stem** (often the 'tens' digits) and numbers in the **leaves** (often the 'units' digits) are aligned to show the shape of the distribution.

Example

A student records the number of text messages she sends each day for 15 days.

21   32   31   10   18   19   25   37

30   34   22   25   34   32   25

a) Show the results in a stem-and-leaf diagram.

Solution A

10, 18, 19, 21, 22, 25, 25, 25, 30, 31, 32, 32, 34, 34, 37 ← Sort the numbers into order

Stem   Leaves

```
1 | 0  8  9
2 | 1  2  5  5  (5)
3 | 0  1  2  2  4  4  7
```

← Put the data into a stem-and-leaf diagram

1 | 0 represents 10 text messages ← Add a key

Solution B

```
1 | 0  8  9
2 | 1  5  2  5  5
3 | 2  1  7  0  4  4  2
```

← Put the data into an unordered stem-and-leaf diagram

```
1 | 0  8  9
2 | 1  2  5  5  (5)
3 | 0  1  2  2  4  4  7
```

← Reorder the values

1 | 0 represents 10 text messages ← Add a key

b) Work out the median.

Solution

The median of the 15 values is the 8th number (circled) when the numbers are ordered, so median = 25

c) Work out the range.

Solution

The range is biggest − smallest = 37 − 10 = 27

Two-way Tables

A **two-way table** is a table that links two sets of information.

The table shows there are 83 boys and 62 girls in year 10 and 75 boys and 94 girls in year 11.

	Year 10	Year 11
Boys	83	75
Girls	62	94

Example

Complete the two-way table using this information about people visiting a theatre:

- Altogether there are 120 adults.
- There are twice as many male adults as female adults.
- Altogether there are 75 females.
- There are 65 male children.

	Male	Female	Total
Adults			
Children			
Total			

Solution

Problem Solving

First fill in the numbers you're given (in this case 120, 65 and 75). Now calculate the missing ones. You're given the total number of adults and the proportion of male adults to female adults, so you can use ratio to find these.

	Male	Female	Total
Adults	80	40	120
Children	65	35	100
Total	145	75	220

120 divided in the ratio 2 : 1 = 80 : 40

Sampling Methods

There are two main ways of sampling a population:
- **Random sampling** – every member of the population has an equal chance of being chosen.
- **Stratified sampling** – the population is divided into categories and the sample is taken using the same proportion in each category as in the population.

To obtain a random sample:
1. give every member of the population a number
2. choose numbers at random, e.g. by picking from a hat.

To obtain a stratified sample:
1. decide the categories to stratify
2. work out the same proportion of each category that gives the correct sample size overall.

Example

There are 43 boys and 57 girls in a year group. A 10% sample stratified by gender is to be chosen for a committee. How many boys and how many girls are on the committee?

Solution

10% of 43 is 4.3; 10% of 57 is 5.7

So 4 boys and 6 girls are chosen.

Use whole numbers to obtain 10% of the total population

Quick Test

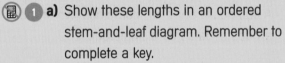

1. a) Show these lengths in an ordered stem-and-leaf diagram. Remember to complete a key.

12 cm	14 cm	28 cm	25 cm
22 cm	11 cm	12 cm	15 cm
18 cm	25 cm	12 cm	

   b) Work out the mode, median and range.

2. The two-way table shows the number of left-handed and right-handed boys and girls in a class.

	Left-handed	Right-handed
Boys	5	8
Girls	6	10

   a) How many boys are in the class?
   b) A child is chosen at random. What is the probability it's a left-handed girl?

3. There are 36 managers, 23 secretaries and 81 manual workers in a factory. A 5% stratified sample is to be chosen by job type for a pay rise. How many of each type will be chosen?

Representing Data

Graphs and Charts

Vertical Line Graphs and Bar Charts

A **vertical line graph** or a **bar chart** can be used to represent discrete data. The height of each line shows the frequency.

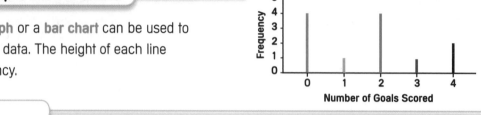

Vertical Line Graph of Goals Scored

Line Graphs

A **line graph** can be used for discrete or continuous data. If the values between the plots have no meaning, the points should be joined with a dashed line as shown.

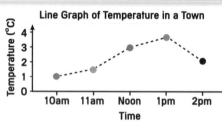

Line Graph of Temperature in a Town

Multiple and Composite Bar Charts

A **multiple bar chart** and a **composite bar chart** show two or more groups of data:

- A multiple bar chart shows two or more groups of data side by side.
- A composite bar chart combines two or more groups of data into a single bar.

A **key** is needed for each group of data.

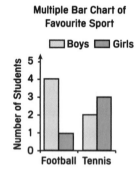

Multiple Bar Chart of Favourite Sport

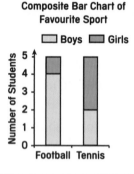

Composite Bar Chart of Favourite Sport

Histograms and Frequency Polygons

A **histogram** or a **frequency polygon** can be used to show continuous data.

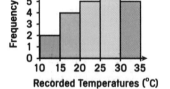

Histogram of Recorded Temperatures

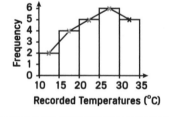

Frequency Polygon of Recorded Temperatures

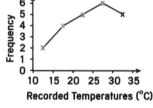

Pie Charts

A **pie chart** can be used to show how parts of a whole are made up. Each part is represented by a sector of a circle. The angle of each sector is proportional to the frequency it represents.

This table of data has been used to create a pie chart.

Favourite Sport

Favourite Sport	Number of Students	Calculation	Angle
Football	7	$\frac{7}{18} \times 360°$	140°
Tennis	3	$\frac{3}{18} \times 360°$	60°
Hockey	8	$\frac{8}{18} \times 360°$	160°
Total = 18			**Total = 360°**

Always check that the angles add up to 360°

Example

The frequency polygons show the lengths of time some students spend on a piece of work.
Compare the times for boys and girls.

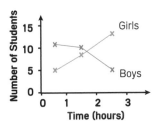

Solution

More girls spent longer on the task.

The total time for girls was approximately
$(5 \times 0.5 + 8 \times 1.5 + 13 \times 2.5)$ hours = 47 hours

The total time for boys was approximately
$(11 \times 0.5 + 10 \times 1.5 + 5 \times 2.5)$ hours = 33 hours

> **Problem Solving**
>
> Write down any true facts but ensure you compare the same facts for boys and girls.

Scatter Diagrams

A **scatter diagram** (**scatter graph**) helps to compare two sets of data by plotting points to represent each pair of variables. **Correlation** describes any trend shown.

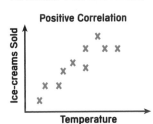

As temperature increases, ice-cream sales increase

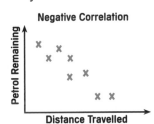

As distance travelled increases, petrol remaining decreases

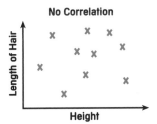

As height increases, there is no trend for length of hair

Line of Best Fit

A **line of best fit**:

* is a straight line through the points
* can be used to estimate unknown values within the range of the points plotted
* is to show the trend — it doesn't have to pass exactly through any of the points.

The correlation is:

* **strong** if the points are very **close** to a line of best fit
* **weak** if the points are more widely **spread**.

Quick Test

1. Draw a pie chart to show the number of people using a shop one day.

Men	Women	Children
36	45	9

2. The table shows the time taken and the distance travelled on eight journeys.

Distance (miles)	Time (minutes)
1.4	3
7.2	15
5.0	8
3.6	6
8.4	13
9.3	12
2.4	5
6.4	11

a) Plot the data on a scatter graph.
b) Draw a line of best fit.
c) Estimate the time taken for a journey of 4 miles.

3. Draw a frequency polygon for this data of the time taken to complete a task.

Time, t (minutes)	Frequency
$0 < t \leq 20$	3
$20 < t \leq 40$	5
$40 < t \leq 60$	2

Further Ways of Representing Data

Cumulative Frequency Diagrams and Box Plots

Cumulative Frequency Diagrams

To draw a **cumulative frequency** graph:

1. work out the running totals of the frequencies
2. plot these totals against the upper class boundaries
3. join the points with either straight lines (cumulative frequency polygon) or a curve (cumulative frequency curve).

Always check that the last running total is the same as the total frequency for the question.

A cumulative frequency graph can be used to work out:

- the median of the data – read off from halfway up the total frequency
- the **lower quartile** – read off from a quarter of the way up the total frequency
- the **upper quartile** – read off from three-quarters of the way up the total frequency
- the **interquartile range**, i.e. upper quartile value – lower quartile value
- the proportion or amount of the data that is above or below a particular value.

Box Plots

Box plots use five key values of the data, namely the minimum value, lower quartile, median, upper quartile and the maximum value.

Example 1

The table shows the time taken for 80 students to travel to school. The shortest time taken is 2 minutes and the longest time taken is 60 minutes.

Draw a cumulative frequency graph and use this to draw a box plot.

Time Taken, T (minutes)	Frequency (i.e. no. of students)	Cumulative Frequency
$0 < T \leqslant 10$	5	5
$10 < T \leqslant 20$	9	$(9 + 5 =)\ 14$
$20 < T \leqslant 30$	16	$(16 + 14 =)\ 30$
$30 < T \leqslant 40$	29	$(29 + 30 =)\ 59$
$40 < T \leqslant 50$	15	$(15 + 59 =)\ 74$
$50 < T \leqslant 60$	6	$(6 + 74 =)\ \boxed{80}$

This matches the total given in the question

Solution

Using the upper class boundaries, plot the points (2, 0), (10, 5), (20, 14), (30, 30), (40, 59), (50, 74) and (60, 80)

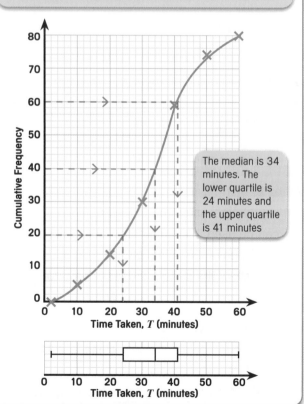

The median is 34 minutes. The lower quartile is 24 minutes and the upper quartile is 41 minutes

Example 2

Use the cumulative frequency graph in Example 1 to work out the percentage of students who take longer than 25 minutes to get to school.

Solution

Problem Solving

You can read off at 25 minutes to see how many students took 25 minutes or less. You can then work out how many took more than 25 minutes and then change this to a percentage.

Reading off at 25 minutes gives 21 students, so $80 - 21 = 59$ students took longer than 25 minutes.

59 as a percentage of 80 is $\frac{59}{80} \times 100 = 74\%$

Histograms

A **histogram** is used to show continuous data.

The **area** of each bar represents the **frequency** for that bar. When the class widths aren't the same the vertical axis is the **frequency density**. So:

Area of bar (frequency of class interval)	=	frequency density	×	width of class interval

$$\text{Frequency density} = \frac{\text{frequency of class interval}}{\text{width of class interval}}$$

Frequency Density = Frequency Divided by class width

Age, A (years)	Frequency	Frequency Density
$0 < A \leq 10$	10	1
$10 < A \leq 20$	20	2
$20 < A \leq 30$	60	6
$30 < A \leq 40$	50	5
$40 < A \leq 60$	60	3
$60 < A \leq 100$	20	0.5

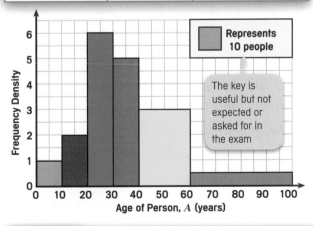

Represents 10 people

The key is useful but not expected or asked for in the exam

Quick Test

1. The test marks of 80 students are shown.

Mark, x	Number of Students	Cumulative Frequency
$0 < x \leq 10$	6	6
$10 < x \leq 20$	12	18
$20 < x \leq 30$	19	
$30 < x \leq 40$	26	
$40 < x \leq 50$	13	
$50 < x \leq 60$	4	

a) Complete the table.
b) Draw a cumulative frequency graph.
c) Work out the median and the interquartile range.
d) The lowest mark was 4 and the highest mark was 55. Draw a box plot to show the data.

2. Draw a histogram for this grouped frequency distribution:

Height, h (cm)	Frequency
$100 < h \leq 102$	8
$102 < h \leq 103$	6
$103 < h \leq 107$	20
$107 < h \leq 110$	9

Probability

Probability Facts

You need to know the following:
- An **event** is anything that you want to use to measure the probability of something happening, e.g. tossing a coin.
- An **outcome** is the result of an event, e.g. getting a head.

- P(A) means the probability of outcome A happening.
- **Equally likely outcomes** each have the same probability of happening, e.g. getting a head or a tail on a fair coin.

Probability of an Outcome

$$P(\text{outcome}) = \frac{\text{number of ways the outcome can happen}}{\text{total number of possible outcomes}}$$

Example

There are 8 boys and 7 girls in a team. The captain is chosen at random.

Write down the probability the captain is a girl.

Solution

There are 7 girls out of 15 in the team, so
$$P(\text{girl}) = \frac{7}{15}$$

Mutually Exclusive Events

Mutually exclusive events are events that have no outcomes in common, e.g. choosing an odd or an even number from a list.

If two events A and B are mutually exclusive:

$$P(A \text{ or } B) = P(A) + P(B)$$

If the probability of an outcome is p, the probability of the outcome not happening is $1 - p$.

Example

In a drawer there are only blue and black socks. The probability of picking a black sock at random is $\frac{3}{5}$.

a) What is the probability of picking a blue sock?

Solution

P(blue) is $1 - P(\text{black}) = 1 - \frac{3}{5} = \frac{2}{5}$

b) There are 4 more black socks than blue socks. How many socks are in the drawer altogether?

Solution

Problem Solving
Start by working out what fraction 4 socks is of all the socks in the drawer. You can then use this fraction to work out the total number of socks.

The probability of picking a black sock is $\frac{1}{5}$ greater than picking a blue sock. So the extra 4 socks must represent $\frac{3}{5} - \frac{2}{5} = \frac{1}{5}$ of the total socks in the drawer.

So there are 4×5
$= 20$ socks in the drawer ← 12 black and 8 blue

Combined Events

A **sample space diagram** can be used to show the possible outcomes from two events, e.g. tossing a coin and throwing a dice.

		Dice					
		1	2	3	4	5	6
Coin	Head	Head, 1	Head, 2	Head, 3	Head, 4	Head, 5	Head, 6
	Tail	Tail, 1	Tail, 2	Tail, 3	Tail, 4	Tail, 5	Tail, 6

$P(\text{Head and 3}) = \frac{1}{12}$

$P(\text{Tail and odd}) \text{ is } \frac{3}{12} = \frac{1}{4}$

Independent Events

Two events are **independent** if the outcome of one event isn't affected by the outcome of the other event.

If two events A and B are independent:

$$P(A \text{ and } B) = P(A) \times P(B)$$

Example 1

A coin is tossed twice. Work out the probability of getting two heads.

Solution

Problem Solving

Tossing a coin twice represents two independent events, so $P(A \text{ and } B) = P(A) \times P(B)$ is the formula to use here. Alternatively you could use a sample space diagram.

$P(HH) = P(H) \times P(H)$

$= \frac{1}{2} \times \frac{1}{2}$

$= \frac{1}{4}$

Example 2

A fair coin is tossed and a fair dice is thrown. Work out the probability of getting a tail and a 3.

Solution

$P(\text{Tail and 3}) = P(\text{Tail}) \times P(3)$

$= \frac{1}{2} \times \frac{1}{6}$

$= \frac{1}{12}$

Same answer as using a sample space diagram

Quick Test

1. Write down the probabilities of the following:
   a) A fair coin landing on heads.   b) Rolling a 1 or a 2 on a fair dice.   c) Rolling a 7 on a fair dice.
2. Two fair dice are rolled. Work out the probability of a total score of 7.

Further Probability

Conditional Probability

Conditional probability describes the probability of events whose outcomes aren't independent. This is sometimes known as **probability without replacement**.

Example

A bag contains six coloured counters. Two are yellow and four are blue.

A counter is taken out and not replaced.

Another is then taken out. ← *This is the same as taking two out together*

Work out the probability that:

a) the first counter is blue

Solution

Four of the six counters are blue

So P(First counter blue) is $\frac{4}{6} = \frac{2}{3}$

b) both counters are blue.

Solution

If the first counter was blue, there are now two yellow and three blue counters left.

So P(Second counter blue) is $\frac{3}{5}$

So P(Both counters blue) is $\frac{2}{3} \times \frac{3}{5} = \frac{6}{15} = \frac{2}{5}$

Tree Diagrams

A **tree diagram** can be used as an alternative method for dealing with problems involving two or more events. The tree diagram has **branches** to show each event.

Example 1

A coin is tossed twice. Use a tree diagram to work out the probability of getting:

a) two heads

Solution
P(HH) = P(H) × P(H) = $\frac{1}{4}$

b) at least one tail.

Solution
P(At least one tail)
= 1 − P(HH) = $\frac{3}{4}$

Or P(At least one tail)
= P(HT) + P(TH) + P(TT) = $\frac{3}{4}$

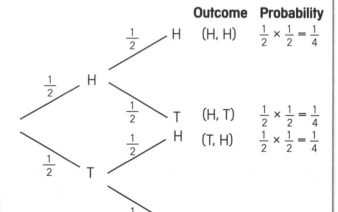

	Outcome	Probability
$\frac{1}{2}$ H	(H, H)	$\frac{1}{2} \times \frac{1}{2} = \frac{1}{4}$
$\frac{1}{2}$ T	(H, T)	$\frac{1}{2} \times \frac{1}{2} = \frac{1}{4}$
$\frac{1}{2}$ H	(T, H)	$\frac{1}{2} \times \frac{1}{2} = \frac{1}{4}$
$\frac{1}{2}$ T	(T, T)	$\frac{1}{2} \times \frac{1}{2} = \frac{1}{4}$

Example 2

A fruit bowl has three red and four green apples. Two apples are chosen at random.

Use a tree diagram to work out the probability of two red apples being chosen.

Solution

Looking at the tree diagram:

$P(RR) = P(R) \times P(R)$

$= \frac{3}{7} \times \frac{2}{6}$

$= \frac{1}{7}$

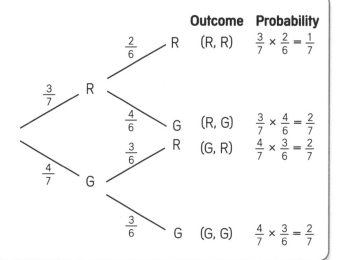

	Outcome	Probability
R	(R, R)	$\frac{3}{7} \times \frac{2}{6} = \frac{1}{7}$
G	(R, G)	$\frac{3}{7} \times \frac{4}{6} = \frac{2}{7}$
R	(G, R)	$\frac{4}{7} \times \frac{3}{6} = \frac{2}{7}$
G	(G, G)	$\frac{4}{7} \times \frac{3}{6} = \frac{2}{7}$

Theoretical Probability, Relative Frequency and Expectation

Probability based on:

- equally likely outcomes is called **theoretical probability**, e.g. P(Head on a fair coin) = $\frac{1}{2}$, as it's assumed that there are two equally likely outcomes (heads and tails)
- the results of an experiment is called **experimental probability** or **relative frequency**:

Relative frequency	=	frequency of a particular outcome
		total number of trials

More trials should give a more reliable result. Relative frequencies can be plotted on a graph against the number of trials to show the trend.

Expectation is the number of times you would expect an event to happen based on the relative frequency or theoretical probability.

Quick Test

1. In a bag there are three red, four blue and three white counters. One counter is chosen at random. A second counter is then chosen at random. Work out the probability that both counters were red:

   a) if the first counter was replaced

   b) if the first counter wasn't replaced.

Example

A five-sided spinner is spun 100 times. Here are the results:

1	2	3	4	5
16	23	32	12	17

a) Write down the relative frequency of landing on the number 4.

Solution

The spinner lands on the number 4 twelve times out of 100, so the relative frequency is $\frac{12}{100}$

b) Do you think the spinner is biased? Give a reason for your answer.

Problem Solving

Compare the relative frequency with the theoretical probability or look at the expectation for the outcomes based on theoretical probability.

Solution

If the spinner is fair, you would expect it to land on each number 20 times (out of 100) but here it lands on 3 thirty-two times. So it appears the spinner is biased because it's more likely to land on 3 than on the other numbers.

Exam Practice Questions

You may wish to answer these questions on a separate piece of paper so that you can show full working out, which you will be expected to do in the exam.

Questions labelled with an asterisk (*) are ones where the quality of your written communication (QWC) will be assessed.

 1. A bag contains white, blue and red counters.

A counter is chosen at random from the bag.

The probability of choosing white is double the probability of choosing red.

The probability of choosing blue is three times the probability of choosing red.

a) Work out the probability that a red counter is chosen.

.... *(3 marks)*

b) Jon says that there are exactly 10 counters in the bag. Explain why he must be wrong.

.... *(1 mark)*

 2. The scatter graph shows the number of driving tests taken to pass and the number of hours of lessons for 13 students.

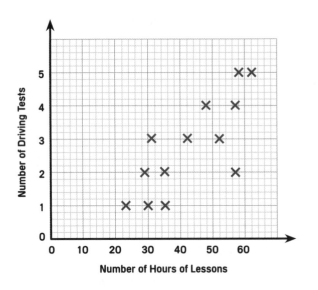

Copy the graph.

a) One of the students had more hours than normal for the number of tests taken. Circle this point on the graph and give a reason why it should be ignored.

.... *(2 marks)*

b) Draw a line of best fit on your graph. *(1 mark)*

c) Describe the relationship between the number of tests taken to pass and the number of hours of lessons.

.... *(1 mark)*

3. When driving to the shops, I go through two sets of traffic lights.

The probability that I stop at the first set is $\frac{1}{4}$. The probability that I stop at the second set is $\frac{2}{3}$.

a) Copy and complete the tree diagram to show the possible outcomes when going through the two sets of lights.

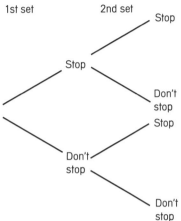

1st set   2nd set

Stop

Stop

Don't stop

Stop

Don't stop

Don't stop

(2 marks)

b) Work out the probability that I stop at both sets of lights.

(2 marks)

4. The box plots show information about the midday temperatures for two holiday towns in September.

Compare the temperatures in town A and town B.

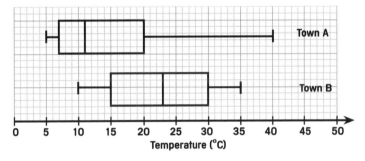

(2 marks)

5. The table shows the weights of 240 parcels collected by a courier.

Weight, w (grams)	Frequency
$0 < w \leqslant 100$	40
$100 < w \leqslant 300$	64
$300 < w \leqslant 500$	86
$500 < w \leqslant 1000$	50

*a) Draw a fully labelled histogram on a piece of graph paper to show this information. *(3 marks)*

b) On the following day, the courier collected 500 parcels. Use the data in the table to estimate the number of parcels that weighed 100 grams or less.

(3 marks)

Answers

Quick Tests

Rounding (pages 4–5)

1. a) i) 18.7   ii) 18.73
        iii) 20   iv) 19
   b) i) 0.1   ii) 0.07
        iii) 0.07   iv) 0.073
   c) i) 2436.5   ii) 2436.52
        iii) 2000   iv) 2400
2. a) 10   b) 20   c) 2000

Multiples and Factors (pages 6–7)

1. a) 14   b) 130   c) 75
2. $60 = 2 \times 2 \times 3 \times 5 = 2^2 \times 3 \times 5$
3. a) 40   b) 28   c) 18
4. a) 4   b) 5   c) 6

Fractions (pages 8–9)

1. a) $4\frac{7}{12}$ b) $1\frac{7}{20}$
   c) 2   d) $1\frac{49}{65}$
2. £40
3. $\frac{1}{20}$

Percentages (pages 10–11)

1. 180 grams
2. 8.33% or $8\frac{1}{3}$%
3. a) £16.80   b) 78 minutes
4. £1125 (to nearest pound)
5. 15

Powers and Roots (pages 12–13)

1. a) 144   b) 27
   c) 13   d) 10
2. a) 6   b) 5
   c) $\frac{1}{2}$ d) $\frac{1}{9}$

Standard Index Form (pages 14–15)

1. a) 3.72×10^2 b) 6×10^3
   c) 2.3×10^{-2} d) 5.67×10^0
2. a) 314   b) 21 000
   c) 0.365   d) 0.058
3. a) 2060 or 2.06×10^3
   b) -1590 or -1.59×10^3
   c) 2 418 000 or 2.418×10^6
   d) 5×10^{-4}

Ratio (pages 16–17)

1. a) 1 : 7   b) 3 : 2
   c) 1 : 20   d) 5 : 1
2. a) 1 : 2   b) 9
3. £16 and £20
4. 90 kg

Proportion (pages 18–19)

1. 12
2. 138.8̇

Upper and Lower Bounds (pages 20–21)

1. a) Upper 54, lower 45
   b) Upper 50.5 mph, lower 49.5 mph
   c) Upper 52.5 cm, lower 47.5 cm
2. Slowest 7.61 m/s, fastest 7.78 m/s

Recurring Decimals and Surds (pages 22–23)

1. a) 0.4   b) 0.4̇   c) 0.2̇30769̇
2. $\frac{7}{33}$
3. a) $3\sqrt{2}$ b) $14 + 6\sqrt{5}$
4. $4\sqrt{2}$

Basic Algebra (pages 24–25)

1. a) $5x$ b) $-4x + 7y$
   c) $-2x^2 + 9xy$ d) $7x - z$
2. a) 5   b) $15\frac{1}{2}$ c) $-2\frac{1}{2}$
3. a) $x = \frac{5y}{2 - y}$ b) $x = \frac{3y + 2}{y - 1}$

Expanding Brackets and Factorising (pages 26–27)

1. $10x + 15$
2. $x^2 - 2x - 15$
3. a) $4x(2x - 3)$ b) $(x - 1)(x - 2)$
   c) $(3x + 4)(x - 5)$ d) $(x - 4y)(x + 4y)$

Linear Equations (pages 28–29)

1. a) $x = 3$ b) $x = 2$ c) $x = -1.25$
2. a) $x = -7$ b) $x = 2$ c) $x = 6$
3. a) $x = 3$ b) $x = 2.75$ c) $x = 4.33$

Quadratic Equations (pages 30–31)

1. a) 2, 9   b) $-\frac{1}{3}$, 5
2. a) $3 \pm \sqrt{5}$ b) $\frac{-3 \pm \sqrt{53}}{2}$
3. a) 1.77, -2.27 b) 2.18, 0.15

Trial and Improvement & Sequences (pages 32–33)

1. a) 2.7   b) 2.8 or 0.6 or -3.4
2. a) i) 20, 23   ii) $3n + 2$ iii) 62
   b) i) 30, 34   ii) $4n + 6$ iii) 86

Straight Line Graphs (pages 34–35)

1. $\frac{3}{2}$, (0, 3)
2. $y = 3x + 1$ and $6x - 2y = 9$ both have gradient = 3, so are parallel.

Linear Inequalities (pages 36–37)

1. a)
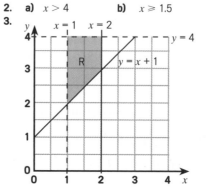

2. a) $x > 4$ b) $x \geqslant 1.5$
3.

Simultaneous Equations (pages 38–39)

1. $x = 5$, $y = 1$
2. $x = 1$, $y = 2$ and $x = 3$, $y = 4$

Harder Equations and Graphs (pages 40–41)

1.

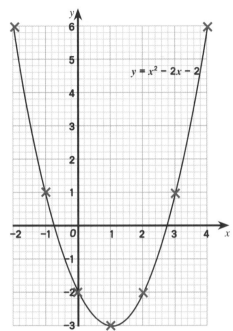

$y = x^2 - 2x - 2$

2. a) 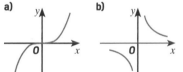 b) c)

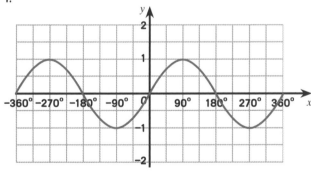

Trigonometrical Graphs and Transformations (pages 42–43)

1.

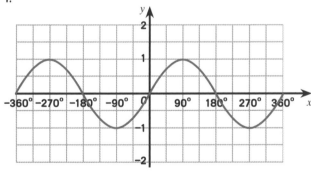

2. Translation of $90°$ in the x-direction.

Angles and Parallel Lines (pages 48–49)

1. a) $126°$; allied angles
   b) $47°$; angles on a straight line and alternate (or corresponding) angles
   c) $21°$; angles on a straight line and alternate (or corresponding) angles

Angles of Polygons (pages 50–51)

1. a) Exterior $45°$, interior $135°$
   b) Exterior $36°$, interior $144°$

Areas of Triangles and Quadrilaterals (pages 52–53)

1. a) 8.05 cm^2 b) 12.65 cm^2
   c) 10.08 cm^2 d) 8.94 cm^2

Circumference and Area of Circles (pages 54–55)

1. a) i) 29.5 cm   ii) 69.4 cm^2
   b) i) 19.2 cm   ii) 29.2 cm^2
   c) i) 15.1 cm   ii) 18.1 cm^2
2. a) i) 10π cm   ii) 25π cm^2
   b) i) 12π cm   ii) 36π cm^2

Arc Length and Area of a Sector (pages 56–57)

1. a) i) 12.0 cm   ii) 36.1 cm^2
   b) i) 6.6 cm   ii) 29.7 cm^2
   c) i) 13.3 cm   ii) 26.5 cm^2

Plan and Elevation (pages 58–59)

1. a) i)   ii)   iii)

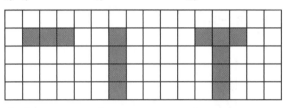

   b) i)   ii)   iii)

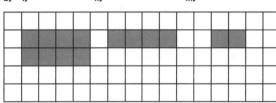

   c) i)   ii)   iii)

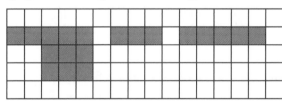

(Accept elevations in either order)

Volumes of Prisms (pages 60–61)

1. a) 60 cm^3 b) 491 cm^3 c) 42 cm^3

Volumes of Pyramids, Cones and Spheres (pages 62–63)

1. a) 25.5 cm^3 b) 64.1 cm^3 c) 34.7 cm^3

Pythagoras' Theorem (pages 64–65)

1. a) 17 cm   b) 8.06 cm   c) 6.24 cm

Surface Area (pages 66–67)

1. a) 54 cm^2 b) 62 cm^2 c) 132 cm^2
   d) 90π cm^2 e) 75.4 cm^2

Trigonometry in Right-angled Triangles (pages 68–69)

1. a) 6.7 cm   b) 11.4 cm   c) $60°$

Sine and Cosine Rules (pages 70–71)

1. a) 15.4 cm   b) $38.7°$
   c) 6.58 cm   d) $36.9°$

Answers

Circle Theorems (pages 72–73)

1. **a)** 32° **b)** 56°
   c) 88° **d)** 65°

Transformations (pages 74–75)

1. **a)** A translation by the vector $\begin{pmatrix} 5 \\ -1 \end{pmatrix}$
   b) A reflection in the line $y = x$
   c) A rotation 90° anticlockwise about (0, 0)

Congruency and Similarity (pages 76–77)

1. SAS
2. 4.8 cm
3. 8 : 27

Vectors (pages 78–79)

1. **a)** $-\mathbf{b} + \mathbf{a}$ **b)** $\mathbf{a} - 3\mathbf{b}$ **c)** $-2\mathbf{a} + 4\mathbf{b}$
2. **a)** $\begin{pmatrix} 2 \\ 2 \end{pmatrix}$ **b)** $\begin{pmatrix} -1 \\ 4 \end{pmatrix}$

Conversions, Bearings and Scale Drawings (pages 80–81)

1. **a)**  **b)** 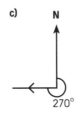 **c)**

Constructions (pages 82–83)

1. Triangle drawn to scale with lengths accurate to ±1 mm
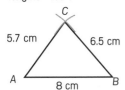

2.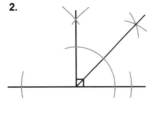

Loci and 3-D Coordinates (pages 84–85)

1. **a)**
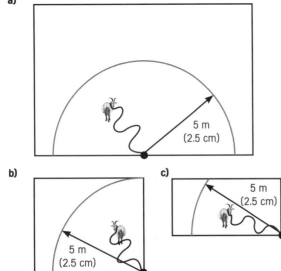

2. **a)** (4, 0, 0) **b)** (4, 3, 0)
   c) (0, 0, 2) **d)** (0, 3, 2)

Handling Data Cycle and Questionnaires (pages 90–91)

1. **Any suitable answer, e.g.** Give each person 10 spellings; record the results; work out the mean number correct for boys and girls separately; compare the means and decide if there is any significant difference in the results.
2. It's a leading question as "Do you agree" is showing bias. It's not possible to say "Don't know".

Averages and Range (pages 92–93)

1. Mode = 4; median = 4.5; mean = 4.65; range = 3
2. Modal class = $2 < x \leq 4$; class containing median = $2 < x \leq 4$; estimate of mean = 3.67

Sorting Data and Sampling Methods (pages 94–95)

1. **a)**

1	1 2 2 2 4 5 8
2	2 5 5 8

   Key: 1|1 represents 11 cm

   b) Mode = 12 cm; median = 15 cm; range = 17 cm

2. **a)** 13 **b)** $\dfrac{6}{29}$
3. 2 managers, 1 secretary and 4 manual workers

Representing Data (pages 96–97)

1. A pie chart should be drawn with angles of: Men 144°; Women 180°; Children 36°
2. **a) and b)**

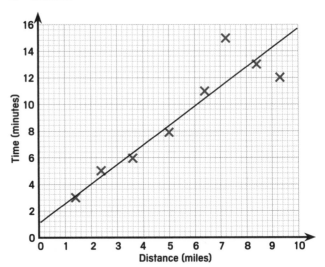

   c) 7 minutes

3.

Further Ways of Representing Data (pages 98–99)

1. **a)** 37, 63, 76, 80

   b)

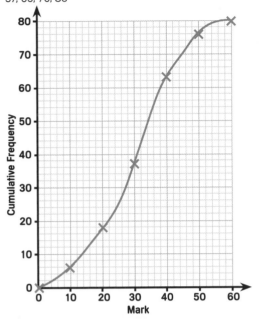

   c) Median = 31, interquartile range = 16

   d)

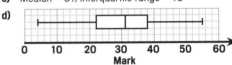

2.

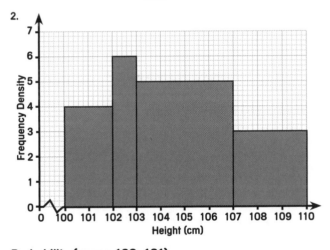

Probability (pages 100–101)

1. **a)** $\frac{1}{2}$ **b)** $\frac{1}{3}$ **c)** 0

2. $\frac{1}{6}$

Further Probability (pages 102–103)

1. **a)** $\frac{9}{100}$ **b)** $\frac{1}{15}$

Exam Practice Questions

*Key: M are marks for method (e.g. **M1** means 1 mark for method); A are accuracy marks (e.g. **A1** means 1 mark for accuracy); B are independent marks that don't require method to be shown (e.g. **B2** means 2 independent marks); Q are marks for quality of written communication (e.g. **Q1** means 1 QWC mark).*

You're encouraged to show your working out, as you may be awarded marks for method even if your final answer is wrong. Full marks can be awarded where a correct answer is given without working being shown but if a question asks for working out, you must show it to gain full marks. If you use a correct method that isn't shown in the mark scheme below, you would still gain full credit for it.

Number and Algebra (pages 44–47)

1. **M1 a)** $8 + 32x - 4x - 12 = 0$ **(One error allowed)**
   M1 $28x - 4 = 0$ or $28x = 4$
   A1 $x = \frac{1}{7}$
   M1 b) $\frac{y}{2} = 11 + 5$ or $\frac{y}{2} = 16$
   A1 $y = 32$

2. **M1** (Fridge World)
   $480 \div 3$ or £160
   or $480 - 160$
   M1 (Fridge Bargains)
   12×25 or £300
   M1 (The Electric Store)
   $\frac{20}{100} \times 300$ or 0.2×300
   or £60
   A2 £320, £340, £360 **(A1 for any two correct prices)**
   Q1 Fridge World (is the cheapest)

   To score the quality of written communication mark you must have shown the method for each calculation.

3. **M1 a)** $6^2 + 5$ or $36 + 5$
   A1 41
   M1 b) $7^2 + 5 = 54$ or $8^2 + 5 = 69$
   or $9^2 + 5 = 86$ or $10^2 + 5 = 105$
   or $11^2 + 5 = 126$
   A1 No, with working shown or reason given, e.g. $n^2 = 120$ doesn't give a whole number answer

   There are lots of valid reasons for answering this part, e.g. 10th term = 105, 11th term = 126 or 125 isn't 5 more than a square number, it's 4 more than a square number.

4. **M1** 7 + 5 or 12 parts seen
   M1 $84 \div 12$ or 1 part = £7
   A1 2 parts = £14
   Q1 She isn't correct

   Must see working to award the quality of written communication mark.

5. **M1 a)** $\frac{16\,500 - 6900}{3}$
   A1 £3200
   M1 b) $6900 - 3200$
   A1 £3700

6. **M1 a)** Factors of 42 shown, e.g. $42 = 6 \times 7$ or $42 = 3 \times 14$ or $42 = 2 \times 21$
   May be on a factor tree:

Answers

A1 $2 \times 3 \times 7$
B1 b) $2^2 \times 3^2 \times 7^2$

7. **M1 a)** Kylie has £$\frac{x}{2}$ or Jack has £$(\frac{x}{2} + 5)$

    A1   Kylie has £$\frac{x}{2}$ and Jack has £$(\frac{x}{2} + 5)$

          So total $20 = x + \frac{x}{2} + \frac{x}{2} + 5$

    M1 b) $2x + 5 = 20$
    M1 $2x = 20 - 5$ or $2x = 15$ or $x = 7.5$
    Q1   £7.50 **(Money notation must be correct)**

8. **M1 a)** $3 + \frac{3}{12} + \frac{8}{12}$

    A1 $3\frac{11}{12}$

    M1 b) $3\frac{1}{3} = \frac{10}{3}$ or $1\frac{1}{2} = \frac{3}{2}$

    M1 $\frac{10}{3} \times \frac{3}{2}$
    A1   5

9. **M1** $120\% = £168$
    M1 $168 \div 1.2$ or $168 \div 120 \times 100$
    A1   £140

10. **B2 a)** $4y(2x - 3y)$ **(B1 for a partial factorisation $2y(4x - 6y)$ or $y(8x - 12y)$ or $4(2xy - 3y^2)$ or $2(4xy - 6y^2)$)**
    B2 b) $(2x + 1)(x - 3)$ **(B1 for $(2x + a)(x + b)$ where $ab = \pm 3$)**

11. **M1 a)** $15\,000 - 5040$ or £9960
          or $14\,400 - 8100$ or £6300

    M1 $\frac{20}{100} \times 9960$ or $\frac{20}{100} \times 6300$
    A1   £1992 and £1260
    Q1   £1992 − £1260 = £732 and Harry

> *Remember to answer the question by stating clearly who pays most tax.*

    M1 b) $15\,000 - 1992$
          or $14\,400 - 1260$
    Q1   £13 008 and £13 140
          Kim takes home £132 more.

> *Remember to answer the question by stating clearly who takes home most pay.*

12. **B1 a)** 1.4×10^6
    B1 b) 300 000 000

13. **B1** $y = 3x + 4$

14. **M1** $I \propto \frac{1}{R}$ or $I = \frac{k}{R}$

    M1 $10 = \frac{k}{24}$ or $k = 240$

    A1 $I = \frac{240}{R}$
    Q1   When $R = 48$, $I = 5$, so current halves

> *Must state that $I = 5$ and current halves to award final mark.*

15. **M1 a)** $9 + 3\sqrt{5} + 3\sqrt{5} + 5$
    A1 $14 + 6\sqrt{5}$

    M1 b) $\frac{10}{\sqrt{2}} \times \frac{\sqrt{2}}{\sqrt{2}}$ or $\frac{10\sqrt{2}}{2}$

    A1 $5\sqrt{2}$

16. **B1 a)**

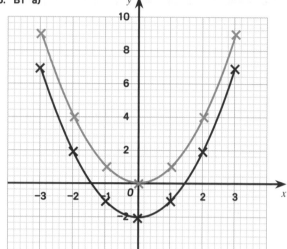

    B1 b) $(-1, 0)$

17. **B2 a)**

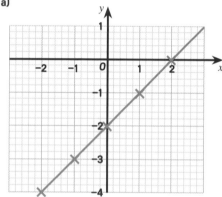

    (B1 for at least two correct points plotted.)
    B1 b) $y = x - 2$

Geometry and Measures (pages 86–89)

1. **M1** $\frac{1}{2}(9 + 4) \times 5$
    A1 32.5 cm²

2. **M1 a)** $x + 34° = 47°$ or $x = 47° - 34°$
    A1 $x = 13°$
    M1 b) $y = 180° - 34°$ or $y = 133° + 13°$
    A1 $y = 146°$

3. **M1** $\pi \times 4 \times 4$ or $\pi \times 4^2$
    A1 50.26...
    B1 50.3 cm² **(Follow through any incorrect answer correctly rounded to 1 d.p. Accept 50.2 cm² if π = 3.14 is used)**

> *It's important that you write down your answer to more than 1 decimal place before rounding, in case you have made an error in your calculation.*

4. **B2 a)** Fully correct sketch **(B1 for any correctly labelled line.)**

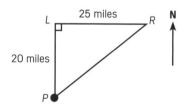

    M1 b) $PR^2 = 20^2 + 25^2$ or $PR^2 = 400 + 625$ or $PR^2 = 1025$

Answers

M1 $PR = \sqrt{1025}$
A1 $PR = 32$ miles or $PR = 32.0$ miles

5. **B1**   Rotation stated

    B1   90° clockwise or $\frac{1}{4}$ turn clockwise

    B1   About O or about $(0, 0)$

6. **B3**   Fully correct triangle drawn **(B1 for side AB 3 cm long, allowing 2.9 to 3.1 cm. B1 for any angle correct, allowing ±2°)**

7. **M1**   Volume of cylinder = $\pi \times 12 \times 12 \times 30$
    A1   Answer in range 13 564 to 13 574
    M1   Area of base of cuboid = 18×16 or 288
    M1 $\pi \times 12 \times 12 \times 30 = 18 \times 16 \times$ height of metal

     or height of metal $= \dfrac{\pi \times 12 \times 12 \times 30}{18 \times 16}$

    A1   Height of metal = 47.1... cm or 47 cm

8. **M1**   Angle $ABD = 128° \div 2$ or angle $ABD = 64°$ (Reason: angle at circumference is half the angle at centre)
    M1   Angle $DBC = 180° - 64°$ or angle $DBC = 116°$ (Reason: angles on a straight line add up to 180°)

    M1 $x = \dfrac{180° - 116°}{2}$ or $x = \dfrac{64°}{2}$ (Reason: isosceles triangle)

    A1 $x = 32°$
    Q1   All reasons given

> *Reasons must be clearly stated in order to be awarded the mark for quality of written communication. It can help to work out angles on the diagram.*

9. **Q1**   Smallest angle is angle A.
    M1 $\text{Cos } A = \dfrac{b^2 + c^2 - a^2}{2bc}$ or $\cos A = \dfrac{7^2 + 6^2 - 5^2}{2 \times 7 \times 6}$
     or
     $5^2 = 7^2 + 6^2 - 2 \times 7 \times 6 \cos A$
    A1 $\text{Cos } A = 0.714...$
    A1 $A = 44.4°$ or $A = 44°$

> *Remember that the smallest angle is opposite the shortest side. Make sure that you keep all the digits on your calculator display to avoid making rounding errors.*

10. **M1**   Angle $A = 180° - 80° - 65°$ or Angle $A = 35°$

    M1 $\dfrac{a}{\sin 35°} = \dfrac{8.4}{\sin 80°}$

    M1 $a = \dfrac{8.4 \times \sin 35°}{\sin 80°}$

    A1   4.9 cm

11. **M1 a)** $(2x + 3)(5x - 3)$
    M1 $10x^2 + 9x - 9$
    A1 $10x^2 + 9x - 9 = 27$
    M1 b) $(ax + b)(cx + d)$ where $ac = 10$ and $bd = \pm36$
    A1 $(2x - 3)(5x + 12)$
    B1 $x = 1.5$ and $x = -2.4$ **(Follow through from incorrect brackets)**

    B1 c)   6 cm

> *Remember that you can't have a negative answer for x as it's a length.*

12. **B1**   Two angles and a corresponding side

Statistics and Probability (pages 104–105)

1. **M1 a)**   White : Blue : Red = 2 : 3 : 1
    M1   Denominator of 6 used

    A1 $\dfrac{1}{6}$

    B1 b)   Valid reason given, e.g. $\frac{1}{6}$ of 10 isn't a whole number or must be a multiple of 6 counters in the bag

2. **B1 a)**   Circle around student at (57, 2)
    B1   Doesn't follow the trend of the rest of the points
    B1 b)   Line of best fit drawn starting at or before (23, 1) to (35, 1) and ending at or after (58, 5) to (62, 5)
    B1 c)   The more tests taken, the more hours of lessons (positive correlation).

3.   **a)**   1st set   2nd set

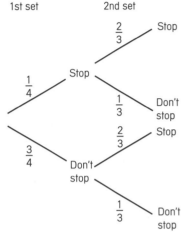

    B1   First branches correct
    B1   Second branches correct

    M1 b) $\dfrac{1}{4} \times \dfrac{2}{3}$

    A1 $\dfrac{2}{12}$ or $\dfrac{1}{6}$

4. **B2**   Any two correct comparisons
    B1 for each, e.g. on average it's hotter in town B (median 23°C in B compared with median 11°C in A); the range of the temperatures in A is bigger than in B (range for A is 40°C − 5°C = 35°C and range for B is 35°C − 10°C = 25°C); interquartile range for the temperatures in A is less than in B (interquartile range for A is 20°C − 7°C = 13°C and interquartile range for B is 30°C − 15°C = 15°C)

> *You'll be expected to compare the medians and a measure of spread. It's not enough to simply state facts without making a comparison.*

5.   **a)**

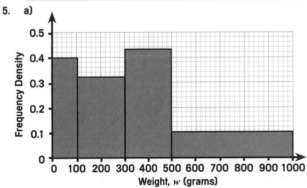

    B1   One bar to correct height or correct calculation shown
    B1   Fully correct bars
    Q1   Axes labelled

> *For the quality of written communication mark to be awarded, all labels must be correct.*

    M1 b) $\dfrac{40}{240}$ or $\dfrac{1}{6}$ seen

    M1 $\dfrac{1}{6}$ of 500

    A1   83

Maths Dictionary

G 3-D coordinates – coordinates that give the height, width and depth of an object; used to identify points in space using x, y and z-axes.

G Acceleration – increase in speed or velocity.

G Acute angle – an angle that lies between 0° and 90°.

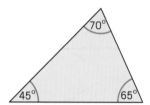

G Adjacent side – the side next to the angle or side being considered.

N Algebraic expression – a statement that uses letters as well as numbers.

G Allied angles – angles that add up to 180°.

G Alternate angles – angles formed when two or more lines are cut by a transversal. If the lines are parallel then alternate angles are equal.

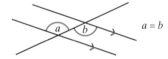
$$a = b$$

G Alternate segment – the 'other' segment. In a circle divided by a chord, the alternate segment lies on the other side of the chord.

G Angle of depression – the angle you have to turn downwards from looking along the horizontal to look at the ground or sea from the top of a tower, tree, cliff, etc.

G Angle of elevation – the angle you have to turn upwards from looking along the horizontal to look at the top of a tree, cliff, etc.

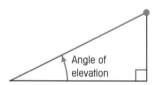
Angle of elevation

G Angles at a point – angles that meet at the same point and add up to 360°.

G Angles on a straight line – two or more angles, at the same point on a straight line, that add up to 180°.

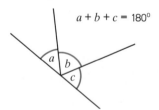
$$a + b + c = 180°$$

N Approximation – an answer that is nearly correct but not exact.

G Arc – a curve forming part of the circumference of a circle.

G Area ratio – the ratio of the areas of two similar shapes is equal to the ratio of the squares of their corresponding lengths.

N S Ascending – going up in order from smallest to largest.

S Average – a single number that represents or typifies a collection of values.

G Average speed – the total distance travelled divided by the total time.

$$\text{Average speed} = \frac{\text{total distance travelled}}{\text{total journey time}}$$

N Balance – keeping one side of an equation the same as the other side.

S Bar chart – a chart that uses bars of equal width to represent discrete data.

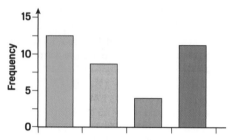

G Bearing – the direction measured clockwise from a North line at a fixed point. A bearing has three digits (for angles less than 100°, a zero, or zeros, is placed in front, e.g. 025°).

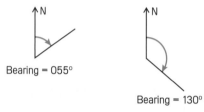
Bearing = 055°

Bearing = 130°

S Bias – a tendency either towards or away from some value; a question that invites a particular response, e.g. Do you agree that smoking is bad for you?

N BIDMAS – an acronym that helps you remember the order of operations: Brackets, Indices and roots, Division and Multiplication, Addition and Subtraction.

G Bisector – a line that divides a line, angle or area exactly in half.

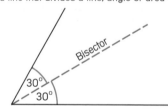
Bisector
30°
30°

S Box plot – a graphic representation of the distribution of a set of data, showing the median, quartiles and the extremes of the data set.

N Cancel – simplifying a fraction by dividing the numerator and denominator by a common factor.

G Capacity – the amount of space in a container or the amount of liquid it will hold.

G Centre – the middle point of something, e.g. the fixed point at the middle of a circle or a sphere.

G Centre of enlargement – the point from which the enlargement happens.

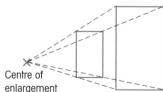
Centre of enlargement

G Centre of rotation – the point around which a shape can rotate.

N Change the subject – rearranging a formula to leave one variable on its own.

ⓖ Chord – a line joining two points on the circumference of a circle.

ⓖ Circumference – the distance all the way round the outline of a circle.

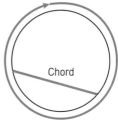

Circumference

Chord

ⓢ Class – the grouping of large amounts of data into different classes.

ⓢ Class interval – the width of a class or group, e.g. 0 g < mass of spider ⩽ 10 g.

ⓝ Coefficient – a number or letter multiplying an algebraic term.

ⓖ Collinear – passing through, or lying on, the same straight line.

ⓝ Common factor – a factor that is shared by two or more numbers.

ⓝ Common multiple – a multiple that is shared by two or more numbers.

ⓝ Complete the square – writing a quadratic expression of the form $x^2 + bx + c$ in the form $(x + p)^2 + q$. This method can be used to solve quadratic equations.

ⓢ Composite bar chart – a bar chart that combines two or more groups of data into a single bar.

ⓝ Compound interest – interest that accrues from the initial deposit plus the interest added on at the end of each year.

ⓝ Compound percentage – a repeated percentage.

ⓢ Conditional probability – the probability that an event will occur given that another event has already occurred.

ⓖ Cone – a shape with a plane circular face, a curved surface and one vertex.

ⓖ Congruent – exactly alike in shape and size.

ⓖ Construction – an accurate drawing of a shape using a combination of ruler, protractor and a pair of compasses.

ⓝⓢ Continuous data – data that can take any value within a given range, e.g. length and time.

ⓖ Conversion – changing from one measure to another, e.g. metric to imperial.

ⓝⓖ Coordinate – a set of two or more numbers used to determine the position of a point, line, curve or plane in a space of a given dimension with respect to a system of lines or other fixed references.

ⓢ Correlation – the relationship between the numerical values of two variables, e.g. there is a positive correlation between the numbers of shorts sold as temperature increases; there is a negative correlation between the age and the value of cars.

ⓖ Corresponding angles – angles formed when a transversal cuts across two or more lines. When the lines are parallel corresponding angles are equal.

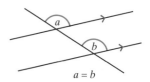

$a = b$

ⓖ Cosine – the cosine of an angle is the ratio of the length of the adjacent side to the length of the hypotenuse in a right-angled triangle.

ⓖ Cosine rule – a formula used to find the lengths of sides or the size of an angle in a triangle. The formula is given on the GCSE exam paper.

$a^2 = b^2 + c^2 - 2bc \cos A$.

ⓖ Cross-section – the shape of a slice through a solid.

ⓝ Cube number – a number that is the product of three equal numbers, e.g. $4^3 = 64$

ⓝ Cube root – the cube root of a number is a number which, when cubed, gives the original number, e.g. $\sqrt[3]{64} = 4$

ⓝ Cubic – a cubic function of the form $y = ax^3 + bx^2 + cx + d$. Graphs of cubic functions are S-shaped.

ⓖ Cuboid – a 3-D shape with six rectangular faces.

ⓢ Cumulative frequency – the running total of frequencies calculated from a frequency table.

ⓖ Curved surface area – the area of the curved surface of a solid such as a cylinder or a cone.

ⓝⓖ Cyclic – a graph that repeats indefinitely in both directions.

ⓖ Cyclic quadrilateral – a quadrilateral with all four vertices on the circumference of a circle.

ⓖ Cylinder – a prism with a circular cross-section.

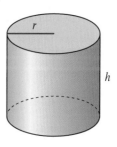

ⓢ Data – a collection of numbers or information.

ⓢ Data collection sheet – a sheet or log that is used to collect data.

ⓖ Decagon – a 10-sided polygon.

ⓝ Decimal place – the position of a digit after the decimal point.

ⓝ Degree of accuracy – the level of approximation that is made, e.g. to the nearest £, cm or thousand.

ⓝ Denominator – the bottom number of a fraction.

ⓝⓖ Density – the ratio of the mass of an object to its volume; the mass per unit volume.

ⓝⓢ Descending – going down in order from largest to smallest.

ⓖ Diameter – a straight line across a circle, from circumference to circumference and passing through the centre.

ⓝ Difference of two squares – the factorisation of $a^2 - b^2$ which equals $(a + b)(a - b)$.

ⓝ Direct proportion – two values or measurements may vary in direct proportion, i.e. if one increases, then so does the other.

ⓝ Directed number – a number that is given a '+' or '−' sign.

ⓝⓖ Direction – the line along which anything lies, faces or moves.

ⓝⓢ Discrete data – data that can only have certain values in a given range, e.g. number of goals scored, shoe sizes.

Maths Dictionary

N G Distance-time graph – a graph that shows how distance varies with time.

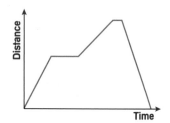

N Elimination – removing a variable from an equation.

G Enlargement – a transformation of a plane figure or solid object that increases the size of the figure or object by a scale factor but leaves it the same shape.

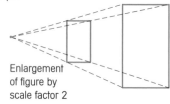

Enlargement of figure by scale factor 2

S Equally likely – the same chance (probability) of two events occurring.

N Equation – a number sentence where one side is equal to the other.

G Equidistant – a point the same distance from two or more other points.

G Equilateral – a 2-D or 3-D shape with all sides of equal length.

N Equivalent fraction – one fraction that has the same value as another fraction, e.g. $\frac{1}{2}$ and $\frac{2}{4}$ are equivalent fractions.

N Estimate – an approximation of an actual value.

N Even number – a number that when divided by 2 gives no remainder, e.g. 2, 10, 54.

S Event – something that happens, e.g. tossing a coin.

N Exact – an answer that is the true value.

N Expand (brackets) – to expand brackets means to multiply them out to get an expression without brackets.

S Expectation – the number of times you would expect an event to happen based on relative frequency (experimental probability) or theoretical probability.

S Experiment – a test or a trial.

N Exponential – containing, involving or expressed as a power (exponent); an exponential function is of the form $y = k^x$.

N Expression – see **Algebraic expression**.

G Exterior angle – an angle outside a polygon, formed when a side is extended.

Exterior angle

G Face – the flat surface or side of a solid shape.

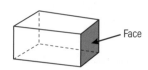

Face

N Factor – a whole number that divides exactly into a given number.

N Factorisation – finding one or more factors of a given number or algebraic expression.

S Fair – an item or event that isn't biased.

N Formula – an equation that enables you to convert or find a value using other known values, e.g. area = length × width.

N Fraction – part of a whole. Fractions can be proper, improper or mixed.

N Fractional power – a fractional power is a root, e.g. $16^{\frac{1}{2}} = \sqrt{16} = 4$ and $8^{\frac{1}{3}} = \sqrt[3]{8} = 2$

S Frequency – the number of times that something happens.

S Frequency density – $\dfrac{\text{frequency of class interval}}{\text{width of class interval}}$

S Frequency polygon – joins the midpoints of data groups or classes in a continuous distribution.

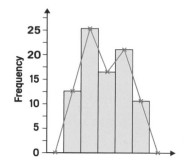

S Frequency table – an arrangement of data in a table.

G Front elevation – the 2-D view of a 3-D shape or object as seen from the front.

G Frustum – the remainder of a regular solid whose upper part has been cut off by a plane parallel to the base.

N Function – a relationship between variables; one variable will depend on the other.

G Geometry – the study of angles, triangles, circles and polygons.

N G Gradient – the measure of the steepness of a slope: $\dfrac{\text{vertical distance}}{\text{horizontal distance}}$

S Grouped data – data that is organised into groups.

G Hemisphere – half of a sphere.

G Hexagon – a six-sided polygon.

N Highest common factor (HCF) – the highest factor shared by two or more numbers.

S Histogram – a chart that is used to show continuous data.

G Hypotenuse – the longest side of a right-angled triangle (always opposite the right angle).

S Hypothesis – a theory that is tested, by investigation, to see if it's true.

N Identity – an identity is similar to an equation, but is true for all values of the variable(s); the identity symbol is ≡, e.g. $2(x + 3) \equiv 2x + 6$

G Image – an object is transformed to give an image, e.g. after a reflection:

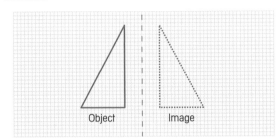

Object   Image

G Imperial (units) – units of weight and measurement, which have generally been replaced with metric units.

N Improper fraction – a fraction in which the numerator is greater than the denominator, e.g. $\frac{9}{4}$

S Independent events – two events are independent if the outcome of one event isn't affected by the outcome of the other event, e.g. tossing a coin and throwing a dice.

N Index (also known as **power** or **exponent**) – the small digit to the top right of a number that tells us the number of times a number is multiplied by itself, e.g. 5^4 is $5 \times 5 \times 5 \times 5$; the index is 4.

N Indirect (inverse) proportion – two quantities vary in indirect proportion when, as one quantity increases, the other decreases.

N Inequality – a statement showing two quantities that aren't equal.

N Input – the value put into a function.

N Integer – any whole number, positive or negative, including zero.

N Intercept – the point where a line or graph crosses an axis.

G Interior angle – an angle inside a polygon between two adjacent sides.

S Interquartile range – the difference between the lower quartile and the upper quartile, often found using a cumulative frequency graph.

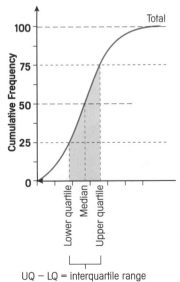

UQ – LQ = interquartile range

N Intersection – the point at which two or more lines cross.

G Irregular – shapes that aren't regular; sides and angles not equal.

G Isometric drawing – a 3-D representation of an object in which the three axes are equally inclined and all lines are drawn to a given scale.

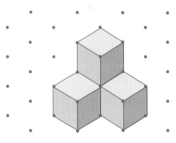

G Isosceles – a triangle with two sides of equal length and two equal angles.

G S Key – a guide on a statistical chart that tells you what each symbol means.

N Least (lowest) common multiple (LCM) – the lowest number that is a multiple of two or more numbers.

N Like terms – terms in algebra that are the same, apart from their numerical coefficients, e.g. $2d$ and $8d$.

N S Limit – a boundary, or the ultimate quantity or extent of something.

N Limits of accuracy – the upper bound and lower bound are sometimes called the limits of accuracy.

S Line graph – a graph where all the plotted points are joined by straight lines, e.g. a graph showing a hospital patient's temperature.

S Line of best fit – a line (usually straight) drawn through the points of a scatter diagram, showing the trend and enabling you to estimate new values using original information.

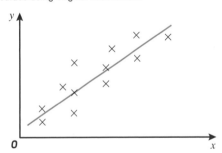

G Line symmetry – the symmetry of a 2-D shape, giving two equal halves.

N Linear equation – an equation that has no variable above the power 1, e.g. $y = 5x + 2$ is a linear equation.

N Linear graph – a graph of a linear function, where all plotted points lie on a straight line.

N Linear inequality – involves a linear expression in two variables by using any of the relational symbols such as $<$, $>$, $\leq$ or $\geq$.

G Locus (plural: loci) – the locus of a point is the path taken by the point following a rule or rules.

N Lower bound – the bottom limit of a rounded number.

S Lower quartile – the reading that is $\frac{1}{4}$ of the way up a cumulative frequency graph or a data set.

N G Magnitude – the size of something.

Maths Dictionary

G Major sector – the larger section of the circle between two radii and an arc.

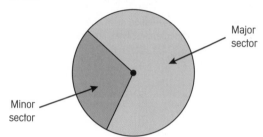

G Major segment – the larger section of the circle between a chord and an arc.

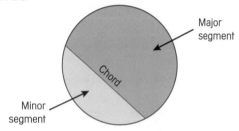

S Mean – an average value found by dividing the sum of a set of values by the number of values.

S Median – the middle item in an ordered sequence of items.

G Metric (units) – units of weight and measure based on a number system in multiples of 10.

G Midpoint – the point that divides a line into two equal parts.

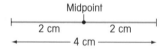

G Minor sector – the smaller section of the circle between two radii and an arc (see **Major sector**).

G Minor segment – the smaller section of the circle between a chord and an arc (see **Major segment**).

N Mixed number – a whole number together with a proper fraction.

S Modal class – the largest class in a grouped frequency table.

S Mode – the most frequently occurring value in a data set.

N Multiple – if one number divides exactly into another number, the second is a multiple of the first.

S Multiple bar chart – a bar chart that shows two or more groups of data side by side.

NG Multiplier – the number by which another number is multiplied.

N Multiply out – see **Expand**.

S Mutually exclusive events – two or more events that can't happen at the same time, e.g. throwing a head and throwing a tail with the same toss of a coin are mutually exclusive events.

NGS Negative number – a number less than zero.

N Negative power – the reciprocal of the same number to the positive power, e.g. $3^{-3} = \frac{1}{3^3} = \frac{1}{27}$

G Net – a surface that can be folded into a solid.

N *n*th term – the general term of a number sequence.

N Number line – a line with a scale, showing numbers in order.

N Numerator – the number above the line in a fraction.

G Object – a shape.

G Obtuse angle – an angle that lies between 90° and 180°.

G Octagon – an eight-sided polygon.

N Odd number – a number that when divided by 2 gives a remainder of 1, e.g. 1, 17, 83.

G Opposite side – the side opposite the angle being worked on in a triangle.

NS Order – the arrangement into which items are put in ascending or descending sequence.

G Order of rotational symmetry – the number of positions where a shape looks the same when it's rotated through 360°.

S Outcome – the result of an event.

NG Parallel – lines that stay the same distance apart and never meet.

G Parallelogram – a quadrilateral with two pairs of equal sides. Opposite sides are parallel and equal in length and the diagonals bisect each other.

G Pentagon – a five-sided polygon.

N Percentage – the proportion or rate per 100 parts.

N Percentage change – the change in the proportion or rate per 100 parts.

G Perimeter – the perimeter of an enclosed area is the boundary or edge of that area; also the length of that boundary.

NG Perpendicular – a line or plane that is at right angles to another line or plane.

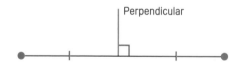

G Perpendicular bisector – a line that is drawn at right angles to the midpoint of a line.

S Pie chart – a circular chart that can be used to illustrate statistical data.

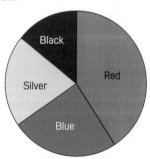

Ⓖ Plan view – the 2-D view of a 3-D shape or object when looking down onto it.

Ground floor of a house

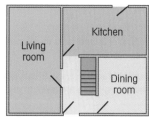

Ⓖ Polygon – a plane (flat) shape with many sides.

Ⓢ Population – the number of people who live in a certain place; any large group of items being investigated.

Ⓝ Position-to-term rule – the rule that links the position of the term to the term, e.g. the position-to-term rule for odd numbers is 'double the position number and subtract 1'.

ⓃⒼⓈ Positive number – a number greater than zero.

Ⓝ Power – see **Index**.

Ⓢ Primary data – data collected by you for an investigation.

Ⓝ Prime factor – is a factor that is also a prime number.

Ⓝ Prime number – has only two factors, itself and 1.

Ⓖ Prism – a 3-D shape that has a uniform cross-section.

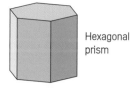

Hexagonal prism

Ⓢ Probability – the probability of an event occurring is the chance that it may happen, which can be expressed as a fraction, decimal or percentage.

$$\text{Probability} = \frac{\text{number of successful events}}{\text{total number of possible events}}$$

Ⓝ Product – the result of two or more numbers being multiplied together.

ⓃⒼ Proof – an argument or explanation that establishes the truth of a proposition.

Ⓝ Proportion – the relationship between things or parts of things with respect to comparative magnitude, quantity or degree.

Ⓖ Pyramid – a solid shape with triangular faces meeting at a vertex.

Ⓖ Pythagoras' theorem – the theorem which states that the square on the hypotenuse of a right-angled triangle is equal to the sum of the squares on the other two sides.

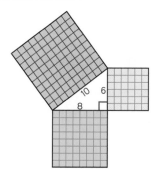

Ⓝ Quadratic equation / expression – an equation or expression containing unknowns with maximum power 2, e.g. $y = 2x^2 - 4x + 3$. Quadratic equations can have 0, 1 or 2 solutions.

Ⓝ Quadratic formula – a formula, given on the GCSE exam paper, used to solve quadratic equations:

$$x = \frac{-b \pm \sqrt{b^2 - 4ac}}{2a}$$

Ⓝ Quadratic graph – the U-shaped graph of a quadratic equation.

Ⓖ Quadrilateral – a four-sided polygon.

ⓃⒼⓈ Quantity – an amount.

Ⓢ Qualitative data – data that is non-numerical, e.g. colour of cars.

Ⓢ Quantitative data – data that is numerical, e.g. number of cars.

Ⓢ Questionnaire – a set of questions used to collect data.

Ⓖ Radius (plural: radii) – the distance from the centre of a circle to its circumference.

Ⓢ Random – something that happens by chance or without bias.

Ⓢ Random sampling – a sampling method where each data object / person has an equal chance of being selected.

Ⓢ Range – the spread of data; a single value equal to the difference between the greatest and the least values.

Ⓝ Ratio – the ratio of A to B shows the relative amounts of two or more things and is written without units in its simplest form or in unitary form, e.g. $A : B$ is $5 : 3$ or $A : B$ is $1 : 0.6$

Ⓝ Rational number – a number that can be written in the form $\frac{a}{b}$ where a and b are integers.

Ⓝ Rationalise – to rationalise an irrational denominator is to make the denominator a rational number. To do this, the numerator and denominator are both multiplied by a surd (square root).

Ⓝ Reciprocal – the reciprocal of any number is 1 divided by the number (the effect of finding the reciprocal of a fraction is to turn it upside down, e.g. the reciprocal of $\frac{2}{3}$ is $\frac{3}{2}$); a reciprocal function is of the form $y = \frac{k}{x}$ with $x \neq 0$

Ⓝ Recurring decimal – a recurring decimal has digits that are in a repeating pattern like 0.3333 or 0.252 525. Recurring decimals are rational numbers.

Ⓖ Reflection – a transformation of a shape to give a mirror image of the original.

Ⓖ Reflex angle – an angle that lies between 180° and 360°.

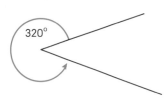

Ⓖ Regular polygon – a polygon that has sides of equal length and equal angles.

Ⓢ Relative frequency – $\frac{\text{frequency of a particular outcome}}{\text{total number of trials}}$

Ⓝ Reverse percentage – involves working backwards from the final amount to find the original amount.

Maths Dictionary

ⓖ Rhombus – a quadrilateral with four equal sides but no right angles (a diamond). Opposite sides are parallel and opposite angles are equal.

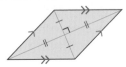

ⓖ Rotation – a geometrical transformation in which every point on a figure is turned through the same angle about a given point.

ⓖ Rotational symmetry – a shape has rotational symmetry if, when rotated through 360°, there are a number of positions where the shape looks the same.

ⓝⓖ Rounding – replacing a number with a nearby number that is easier to work with or better reflects the precision of the data, e.g. 12 964 rounded to the nearest thousand is 13 000.

ⓢ Sample – a section of a population or a group of observations.

ⓢ Sample space diagram – a probability diagram that contains all possible outcomes of an experiment.

ⓝⓖ Scale – a marked measuring line.

ⓖ Scale drawing – a diagram drawn to a given scale.

ⓖ Scale factor – the ratio by which a length or other measurement is increased or decreased.

ⓖ Scalene – a triangle that has no equal sides or angles.

ⓢ Scatter diagram – a statistical graph that compares two variables by plotting one value against the other.

ⓢ Secondary data – data used for investigation that has been collected by another person.

ⓖ Sector – see **Major sector** and **Minor sector**.

ⓖ Segment – see **Major segment** and **Minor segment**.

ⓖ Semicircle – half of a circle.

ⓝ Sequence (or series) – a collection of terms following a rule or pattern.

ⓖ Side elevation – the 2-D view of a 3-D shape or object as seen from the side.

ⓝⓖ Significant figure – the number of digits in a number giving a required degree of accuracy.

ⓖ Similar – the same shape but a different size.

ⓝ Simplify – making something easier to understand, e.g. simplifying an algebraic expression by collecting like terms.

ⓝ Simultaneous equations – two or more equations that are true at the same time; on a graph the intersection of two lines or curves.

ⓖ Sine – the sine of an angle is the ratio of the length of the opposite side to the length of the hypotenuse in a right-angled triangle.

ⓖ Sine rule – in any triangle the ratio of the length of a side to the sine of the opposite angle is constant, so $\dfrac{a}{\sin A} = \dfrac{b}{\sin B} = \dfrac{c}{\sin C}$. The formula is given on the GCSE exam paper.

ⓝⓖ Speed – how fast something moves.

ⓖ Sphere – a 3-D ball shape in which all points of its surface are equidistant from its centre.

ⓖ Square – a quadrilateral that has four equal sides and four right angles.

ⓝ Square – to square a number is to multiply it by itself.

ⓝ Square number – a number that is the product of two equal factors, e.g. $25 = 5^2$

ⓝ Square root – the square root of a number is the number that, when squared, gives that number, e.g. $\sqrt{25} = 5$

ⓝ Standard index form (standard form) – a shorthand way of writing very small or very large numbers; these are given in the form $a \times 10^n$, where a is a number between 1 and 10.

ⓢ Statistics – a collection of data used for analysis.

ⓢ Stem-and-leaf diagram – a semi-graphical diagram used for displaying data by splitting the values.

ⓢ Stratified sampling – a sampling method where the population is divided into categories and a sample is taken using the same proportion in each category as in the whole population.

ⓝ Substitution – to exchange or replace, e.g. in a formula.

ⓖ Subtend – an arc or line segment between two points is subtended by an angle.

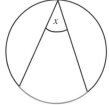

ⓝ Surd – a number written as a square root, e.g. $\sqrt{3}$. A surd is an exact number.

ⓖ Surface area – the area of the surface of a 3-D shape, equal to the area of the net of that shape.

ⓢ Survey – a collection of data for statistical analysis.

ⓖ Symmetry – a 2-D figure can have rotational or line symmetry; a 3-D shape can have rotational or plane symmetry.

ⓖ Tangent – a straight line that touches the circumference of a circle at one point only.

ⓖ Tangent – the tangent of an angle is the ratio of the length of the opposite side to the length of the adjacent side in a right-angled triangle.

ⓝ Term – in an expression, any of the quantities connected to each other by an addition or subtraction sign.

ⓝ Terminating decimal – a decimal fraction with a finite number of digits, e.g. 0.75

ⓝ Term-to-term rule – a rule that links one term to the next term, e.g. the term-to-term rule for even numbers is 'add 2'.

ⓖ Tessellation – a pattern made by fitting together plane shapes (usually regular) without gaps.

ⓢ Theoretical probability – a predicted probability; calculated using the fraction $\dfrac{\text{number of particular outcomes that can happen}}{\text{number of outcomes that are possible from the task}}$

ⓖ Three-figure bearing – see **Bearing**.

ⓖ Transformation – an action such as a translation, reflection, rotation or enlargement.

Ⓖ Translation – a transformation in which all points of a plane figure are moved by the same amount and in the same direction. The movement can be described by a vector.

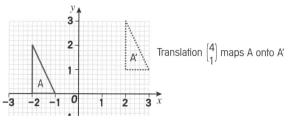

Translation $\begin{pmatrix} 4 \\ 1 \end{pmatrix}$ maps A onto A'

Ⓖ Trapezium – a quadrilateral with just one pair of parallel sides.

Ⓢ Tree diagram – a way of illustrating probabilities in diagram form. It has branches to show each event.

Ⓢ Trial – a test or an experiment.

Ⓝ Trial and improvement – a method of solving an equation by making an educated guess and then refining it step-by-step to get a more accurate answer.

Ⓖ Triangle – a three-sided polygon.

Ⓖ Triangular prism – a prism with a triangular cross-section.

Ⓖ Trigonometry – the branch of maths that shows how to explain and calculate the relationships between the sides and angles of triangles.

Ⓢ Two-way table – a data-handling table to illustrate two variables.

Team

		Red	Blue	Green
	7	16	18	16
Year	8	15	17	16
	9	15	15	15

Ⓝ Ⓖ Unit – means one, a single thing or number; the place-value position immediately to the left of the decimal point.

Ⓝ Unit fraction – a fraction with the numerator 1, e.g. $\frac{1}{3}$, $\frac{1}{27}$

Ⓝ Upper bound – the top limit of a rounded number.

Ⓢ Upper quartile – the reading that is $\frac{3}{4}$ of the way up a cumulative frequency graph or a data set.

Ⓝ Ⓢ Variable – a quantity that can have many values, usually written as a letter, e.g. x, a, k.

Ⓝ Ⓖ Vector – a quantity with both magnitude and direction, e.g. velocity, force, displacement.

Ⓖ Velocity – a more formal, and more correct, way of describing speed using both a magnitude and a direction, e.g. 30 mph towards the North.

Ⓖ Vertex – in 2-D a point where two or more lines meet. In 3-D the corners of a shape, where the edges meet.

Ⓢ Vertical line graph – a graph using vertical lines that can be used to represent discrete data.

Ⓖ Vertically opposite angles – vertically opposite angles are formed when two straight lines intersect. The four angles add up to 360°.

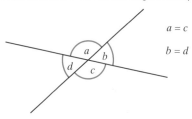

$a = c$

$b = d$

Ⓖ Volume – the amount of space occupied by a substance or object or enclosed within a container.

Ⓖ Volume ratio – the ratio of the volumes of two similar shapes is equal to the ratio of the cubes of their corresponding lengths.

Formulae Sheet

Area of a trapezium $= \frac{1}{2}(a + b)h$

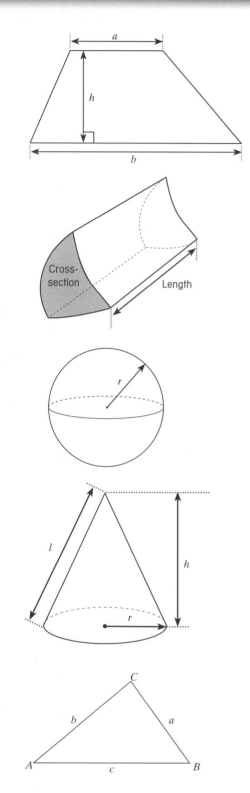

Volume of a prism = area of cross-section × length

Volume of a sphere $= \frac{4}{3}\pi r^3$

Surface area of a sphere $= 4\pi r^2$

Volume of a cone $= \frac{1}{3}\pi r^2 h$

Curved surface area of a cone $= \pi r l$

In any triangle ABC

Area of a triangle $= \frac{1}{2}ab \sin C$

Sine rule $\dfrac{a}{\sin A} = \dfrac{b}{\sin B} = \dfrac{c}{\sin C}$

Cosine rule $a^2 = b^2 + c^2 - 2bc \cos A$

The Quadratic Equation

The solutions of $ax^2 + bx + c = 0$, where $a \neq 0$, are given by

$$x = \frac{-b \pm \sqrt{(b^2 - 4ac)}}{2a}$$